THE WORLD OF THE ANT

LIVING WORLD BOOKS
John K. Terres, Editor

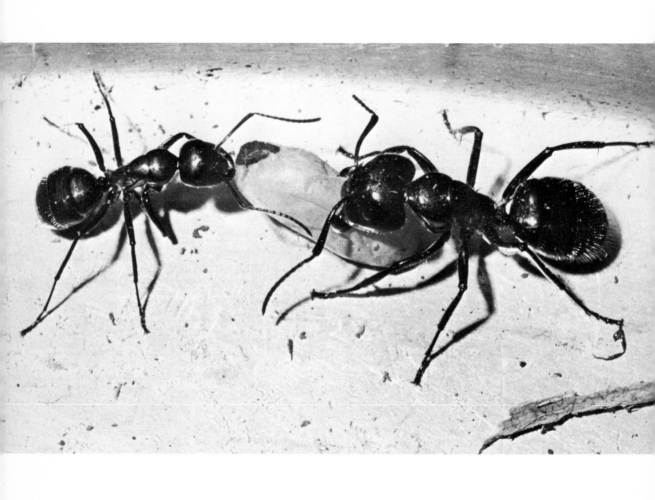

The World of the Ant

Text and Photographs by
David F. Costello

J. B. LIPPINCOTT COMPANY
Philadelphia & New York

To Barbara, David, and Donald, who always have been tolerant of my preoccupation with nature

Contents

Introduction

I HAVE NEVER FOUND anyone who was not interested in ants, in one way or another. Ants are so numerous and so universally distributed that we encounter them in childhood and see them throughout our adult lives. Ants, however, are such small creatures that few people are aware of their unusual attributes, their fascinating social habits, their place in nature's web of life, and their impact on human beings.

There are thousands of kinds of ants. No man could know them all or intimately study the habits and activities of more than a few. Hence, much of what I have written here is based on the observations of ant scientists, or myrmecologists, who have recorded their findings during the last 150 years or more. My own observations, over a period of 30 years, have dealt mainly with the larger species of ants since their little worlds are easier to see.

It is not possible personally to acknowledge the help of all the people who have shared in my work with ants and other wild creatures. People who are enthusiastic about your work because you are enthusiastic are the ones you cherish as real and lasting friends.

I do want to thank Robert L. Furniss of Portland, Oregon, for the loan of insect literature and for aid in wasp identification; William Huber of Atlanta, Georgia, and John C. Moser of Louisiana for information on fire ants and town ants; and Milton Moore of Australia for information on the bull ant. A personal friend, Wally Guy, helped immeasurably on the extreme photographic enlargements of ant heads.

I am especially grateful to John K. Terres, my editor, for his many

13

suggestions and for his expert help in my book writing career.

And although my wife, Cecilia, occasionally had to pick up escaped ants from the living room floor with the vacuum cleaner, she cried when she inadvertently poisoned some of my pet ants that had lived in a cage in my study for a year. I want to say here how I have appreciated her help and her patience.

David F. Costello

Portland, Oregon
November, 1967

Meet the Ant

In Proverbs xxx.25, we read that ants are feeble people. Yet they inhabit most of the land portions of the earth. They are recognized by people of all ages in all countries. But they are among the least understood and least appreciated of all small creatures. Many of their activities and the instinctive behavior in their societies still are largely unsolved riddles.

Ant societies are essentially female societies. The males live only until the marriage flight is done. Few worker ants have ever seen their fathers. But some queens live for many years and lay eggs that hatch into as many as ten million female workers during the lives of their colonies.

These workers clean and feed their queens and act as nursemaids in care of the young in nurseries. They feed the colony, bury the dead, fight mighty battles with scimitarlike jaws, defend themselves and their homes with chemical warfare, and navigate by scent trails or by polarized light.

They build nests of paper, stone, wood, leaves, and silk. They infiltrate, conquer, and enslave colonies of other ants. They construct underground or tree cities with hundreds or even thousands of rooms. They permit insect guests and other intruders to live peacefully in their midst. They make ant bread, grow fungi, and chirp like crickets.

For about one hundred million years they have practiced the purest communism the world has ever known—all for one and one for all. There are no poverty classes among ants. They give and share alike. Their societies have been compared with human society. But they lack one element that characterizes human society: culture.

15

Carpenter ant worker guarding cocoon.

There are ten thousand kinds of ants and therefore ten thousand kinds of ant worlds. Each kind of ant occupies a different niche, depending on its adaptability to different conditions of temperature, moisture, food supply, vegetation cover, and soil or substratum for home construction.

Home for the ant is where the queen and her subjects live. Home is a little hole six inches deep in the ground with as few as a dozen occupants. Home is an earthen mound three feet high in the western desert with ten thousand workers collecting seeds, tending the queen and the nursery, and performing feats of engineering construction in the ant city. Home is a tree in the Brazilian jungle, defended so fiercely by its inhabitants that no creature dares to climb. Or home is the expanse of African landscape where an ant army of millions bivouacs at night and marches each day, routing all things great and small.

16

Meet the Ant

There is no need to go far from where you are at the moment to study the fantastic habits of ants. In season, you can see them when you step off the plane at Fiumicino Airport in Rome, in a bull thorn in Quintana Roo in Mexican Yucatan, in your garden in Vermont, or under a stone in Oregon.

For those of us who will pause to learn some of the physical, chemical, and biological relationships in the little worlds of the ants, there is the likelihood of being amazed at the complexity of life and the interdependence of all creatures that help make up our own larger world. If we can do nothing else, we can momentarily brush away the cares of life by seeing ants as old friends we once knew when we still possessed our wonderful childhood curiosity about living moving things.

My own acquaintance with ants began early. In my tasks as a small

World of the big ants: Squaw Butte in central Oregon.

Formica ants identifying one another. Note segments in antenna of upper ant.

boy on our eastern Nebraska farm, I encountered them and immediately became aware of their mutual cooperation and their togetherness.

One of my jobs on the farm was to make butter in an old crockery churn. When the butter finally "came," I had to work out the water with a wooden paddle and then mold the butter into one-pound chunks to be stored in our outside storm cellar. Sometimes I forgot to cover the butter. Soon, a little black grease ant would appear. Next, a long foraging line would develop. Then there would be hundreds or even thousands of ants on the butter.

I did not know then that an ant has no power or mechanism for survival alone. Unlike spiders, woodchucks, bears, eagles, frogs, and a

Oak galls created by the sting of wasps exude a sweet substance that ants relish.

thousand other animals, ants are not self-sufficient. Even when an ant is temporarily alone, the job it is doing is essential for its own community or society.

The success of ant societies is the result in part of all citizens in every ant city always being on a "first name" basis. This recognition, or identification of one individual by another, appears at times to be carried almost to the point of absurdity. We would have an analogy in human society if, for example, every person on Broadway in New York City stopped to touch and identify every other person. This kind of eternal vigilance among ants, however, is the price they pay for keeping their territories clear of enemies.

19

The World of the Ant

Cooperation among ants is never demonstrated better than when they are defending their cities, engaging in mighty battles with strange ants, or foraging in vast armies for insect and animal food. Some ant colonies, such as the honey ants of the Garden of the Gods in Colorado, have workers that allow their bodies to be stuffed with the sweet liquid from oak galls while they hang from the ceilings of underground chambers month after month. They are the storage bins for their sisters, which need food when it is no longer in season outdoors.

Ants are among the smallest of living things and among the strongest for their size. They are fierce in combat yet solicitous of one another at home. They are intelligent, to a degree, but are bound by instinct to tasks

Formica queen and workers temporarily anesthetized by chloroform.

and accomplishments so amazing as to be almost beyond belief.

Just what is an ant? As members of the animal kingdom they belong to the phylum Arthropoda, which includes mites, ticks, scorpions, crayfish, spiders, and insects. Animals in this phylum have jointed legs and an external skeleton made of cuticle to which the muscles are attached internally. The cuticle occurs in separate pieces or plates as in a suit of armor. The body is divided into segments and the plates are grouped according to the segmentation.

Among arthropods, the ants belong in the class Insecta and to the order Hymenoptera, which includes other social insects such as bees and wasps. Ants themselves have their own family, Formicidae, which is divided into subfamilies, not all of which are found in any one part of the world. The ant family comprises some 350 genera and an estimated ten thousand species and varieties.

Ants are not termites. Termites are social insects that live in colonies in wood or underground and seldom expose themselves to the light of day. Termites have reproductive forms, males and females, with two pairs of whitish, opaque wings of equal size. Ants have males and queens with two pairs of transparent wings of unequal size. Termite adults are grayish white and have thick waistlines. Ant adult workers are of various colors—red, black, yellow, brown, green, or combinations of these—and have thin waistlines.

Male and queen ants, which are the only forms that have wings, do not necessarily resemble each other. Usually the females are larger, sometimes so much larger that the unwary observer might conclude that different species have become mixed in the same nest. All worker ants, regardless of size or special adaptations, are infertile females.

Ants do not grow larger, once their exoskeletons have hardened into armorlike coverings. Small ants, which may be only one tenth the size of their companions in the same nest, are not juveniles. The different sizes, forms, or castes of ants within a given species has been the subject of study by scientists for many years.

Formica *ants guarding the entrance to their nest in a ponderosa pine log.*

The giant among ants seems to be the two-inch-long Tocandira, which lives in South America. In contrast, one of the small parasitic ants that lives in the walls between the burrows of larger ants is only one twenty-fifth of an inch long.

Since their armor is jointed, ants are capable of considerable tortion and twisting. They can double up and touch their tailends with their mandibles. They can bite and then curl their abdomens under their heads to squirt chemicals into the wounds made by the mandibles.

They can twist their heads in various directions to see nearby movements of objects and to regurgitate honeydew or liquid food for other ants on demand. They can stand nearly erect on three legs when danger appears to threaten. And they can fold their legs and appear to be dead when they sleep.

22

Meet the Ant

Many people believe that ants work constantly, because they are usually seen in motion. Actually, ants are experts in the art of the siesta. And being creatures of rhythm they have times for hunting, eating, nest construction, and sleeping. The time of day or night for these activities varies with different kinds of ants and their different surroundings.

The slumber of the wood ants, *Formica rufa,* that I keep in a glass cage is so sound that several vigorous taps on the glass wall are necessary to awaken them and bring them to their feet in furious action.

Ants are among the cleanest of insects. They spend much time cleaning their antennae with special hair combs on their legs. They clean their legs by pulling them through their mandibles or by rubbing their legs together. Ants also lick one another with their tongues as part of their grooming activity.

All property in an ant city is community property. If an ant demands food from a worker returning from far afield, food is given. If I give water to a few of my observation ants, soon they divide it by regurgitation among all the ants in the nest.

Ants can, and do, change jobs from day to day. An ant one day may truck food from the far distant country to the ant city. The next day it may dig tunnels, fight enemies, cut up meat for the colony larder, or tend the ant cemetery like a sexton. And on cold clear days, hordes of wood ant workers may stand idle on top of the nest in the sun soaking up heat that is carried by their bodies into the nest and the nursery chambers.

In my years of observing ants I have found it useful to know how they are put together and how their internal anatomies function. This knowledge has enabled me to identify many of the common ants at sight or with a hand lens. And it has helped me to understand their activities and social life as I have followed them on hand-and-knee expeditions into their own little worlds.

The ant's body has three main parts: the head, thorax, and abdomen. The head is connected to the thorax by a thin neck that is not always readily apparent to the naked eye. The thorax is connected to the abdomen by a "waist" or narrow joint called the pedicel. Actually, the pedicel, which consists of two segments in primitive forms of ants and one segment in advanced forms, is the constricted front end of the abdomen. When the pedicel consists of only one segment it is called the petiole. The enlarged part of the abdomen is called the gaster.

For people interested in further details, the thorax in ants has three parts; the prothorax or part next to the head, the mesothorax or middle part, and the epinotum or rear part. The epinotum is the first segment of the abdomen and in ants is firmly fused to the mesothorax. The upper surface of the prothorax is called the pronotum.

The ant's three pairs of legs are attached to the thorax. The legs are jointed and capable of a wide variety of movements. The leg parts, beginning with the part attached to the thorax, are the coxa, femur, tibia, and metatarsal, with several tarsal joints, the last of which ends in a pair of claws. The two forelegs each have combs or cleaners composed of hairs that are lubricated by glands.

A full-face view of the ant's head shows several important features. Most ants have a pair of large compound eyes situated on the sides of the head. Some ants, in addition, have three simple eyes, or ocelli, located in the middle of the forehead. A few species of ants, including army ants, which do a great deal of marching, are blind.

Much of the ant's knowledge of its world is obtained through its two antennae. Each consists of two parts: the scape or long shaft, which is attached to the head, and the funiculus, which consists of nine to thirteen joints, depending on the species of ant. In spite of the cartoonists, who love to draw caricatures of ants, the antennae do not grow out of the top of the ant's head. Instead, each is attached to the lower front part of the head by a sort of ball and socket arrangement in a depressed area known as the antennal fossa.

The antennae are extremely mobile. When the ant is awake the antennae are in almost constant motion. The olfactory cones and touch

Parts of the ant, left to right: gaster, petiole, epinotum, mesothorax, prothorax, head, antennae.

View of a carpenter ant from below, showing how the legs are attached to the thorax.

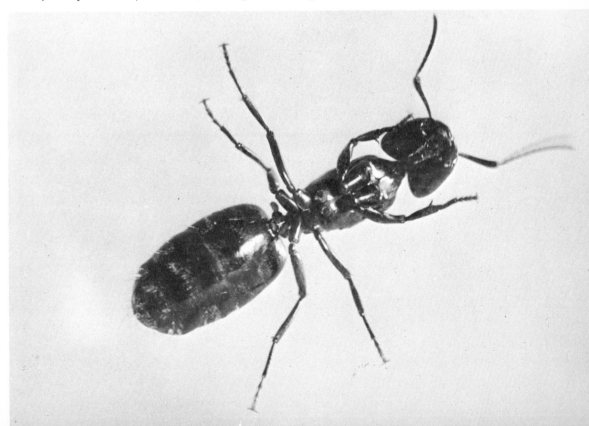

bristles on the antennae enable the ant to feel and examine objects, other ants, enemies, and to smell food and chemical trail or alarm substances.

On the lower part of the ant's face, about where the lips and chin of a human would be, is a plate called the clypeus. The shape of the clypeus is distinctive among different species and is an aid in their identification. Various kinds of ridges and hairs on the heads of ants also give them characteristic features.

The mandibles are the mouth parts we can see with our naked eyes. These jaws or pincers move sideways, and, by means of toothlike protuberances on their inner edges, ants can grasp food, stones, sticks, and enemies or carry eggs, larvae, pupae, and other ants. Carpenter ants excavate tunnels in wood with their mandibles, but they never eat wood. Queen ants sometimes wear off the teeth on their mandibles and thus become "toothless" while digging their new homes.

A second and smaller pair of jaws, the maxillae, which have taste organs, are used for chewing food into small particles. These particles are not swallowed but their juices are squeezed out and the resulting pellet is cast out of the ant's mouth. The ant has a small upper lip, a broad lower lip, and a tongue that it can protrude.

Inside, the ant is more wonderfully constructed than it is outside. Packed within its head and body are nerves and sensory devices that exceed in number and complexity all the transistors and tubes in a thousand television sets.

Inside is a chemical and glandular system that scientists still are trying to understand. And inside are respiratory, circulatory, and digestive systems that enable ants to live efficiently in their chosen niches.

The ant's abdomen contains the sex organs, various glands for manufacturing scents and defense chemicals, and two "stomachs." The first stomach, or crop, is an elastic bag that can be filled with liquid food until the plates on the outside of the abdomen are stretched far apart.

The crop is sometimes called the social stomach, since it holds food for all the other individuals of the colony. Food from this tank can be

Head of a thatching ant, showing two compound eyes and three simple eyes.

Note mandibles of thatching ant. The antennae are attached just above the clypeus.

Formica *ant head.*

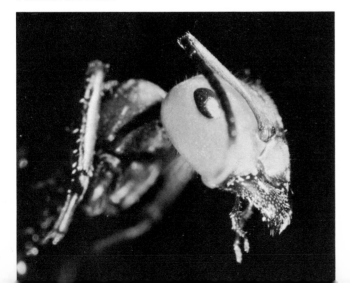

The world of the ant is a miniature jungle. Two ants on an odor trail.

pumped, or regurgitated, into the mouths of the ant larvae and of the adults. For its own digestive purposes, the ant pumps food from the crop into its true stomach.

The senses of ants, as of other animals, might be surmised from a consideration of the niches in which they live. The whole sense world of an ant—sight, sound, smell, feeling—is essentially an area within one inch or less of the insect.

The ant has no need for the eyes of an eagle since its world is one of near horizons. Sheer numbers, ferocity, and a highly developed sense of smell have made eyes unnecessary for army ants. Harvester ants, on the other hand, which live on open terrain and spend much time in individual exploration for seeds, are sensitive to shadows and light changes produced even by remote causes.

Many ants are extremely sensitive to vibrations and to sounds that cause vibrations in the substratum on which they work. The sound of my voice when I say "Hello!" alerts the thatching ants in the glass cage on

Some ants have many hairs, which are sensitive to objects in the ant's surroundings.

Rear view of a Formica ant. The arrangement of hairs is used by scientists to identify different groups of ants.

Harvester ants at the entrance to their nest.

my desk. Sometimes they run into their burrows. More frequently they rear up, stand in a waiting attitude, and attack vigorously any moving object that is brought within half an inch of their heads.

They do not run in confusion unless a general chemical alarm has been given or catastrophe has vastly disturbed the arrangement of their nest. Their senses do not permit them to comprehend what is happening beyond their world. So they react to or attempt to control only that which occurs in their immediate vicinity.

Although most tactile sensations seem to be received by the antennae and mouth parts, ants have numerous sensitive hairs on all parts of their bodies. The sense of taste is well developed. Ants also have temperature senses and kinesthetic senses.

Ants have no voices. Many species, like grasshoppers and katydids,

Harvester ants carrying rabbitbrush seed into mound.

produce sounds by stridulatory organs that are audible to human beings. Ants, however, do not have ears and it has never been proved that they have hearing organs.

Scientists have disagreed for many years about the instincts and intelligence of ants. They do agree that ants have a certain plasticity of behavior in the presence of new situations and that they are capable of learning.

Many years ago, William Morton Wheeler (1910) pointed out that the ant's ability to distinguish between friend and enemy is a matter of learning rather than an inherited reflex. When ants are young they learn to recognize the colony odor. If enemies acquire the colony odor, the ants treat them as friends.

Ants have memories for places and objects. But they have no reasoning power. When faced with a detour problem—food, for example, that the ant can smell and could easily reach by dropping from a platform to the floor half an inch below—the ant will take the long and hard way around.

Recent studies indicate that ant societies are organized principally by complex systems of chemical signals. Responses to odors and glandular substances have become highly specialized in ants through evolutionary development. Basically, however, many of these responses still may be instinctive.

Instinct probably explains why the fungus ant queen packs a pellet of fungus hyphae on her marriage flight and does not expel it until the cell of her new home has been excavated in the ground. Without the fungus, her new family would have no food.

Not so simple is the explanation of why two ants working together will perform more than twice the work done by the same two ants working separately. Is this a chemical stimulus? Is it an awareness of each other's presence and a tendency toward imitation? Or is it cooperation? There is much we do not know about ants.

We do know that the strength of ants is legendary. Most any ant can lift ten times its own weight. Some can lift objects fifty times their own weight. The thatching ants, *Formica rufa obscuripes,* in one of my observation colonies regularly drag four-inch-long Douglas fir twigs to the top of their three-foot-high nest. The ants themselves are less than one third of an inch in length.

One can easily observe feats of endurance and persistence in ants at work. One day in the Blue Mountains of eastern Oregon, I marked a *Formica* ant with a tiny spot of finger nail polish and watched it follow a beaten trail to aphids being tended in a fir tree some two hundred feet from the nest. The marked ant made four trips during the day and once carried home a dead caterpillar at least five times its own weight. In all, I estimated that it traveled fifteen thousand times its own length.

If a six-foot two-hundred-pound man had proportionate endurance and persistence, he would have to run 68 miles in about six hours and carry a one-half-ton load for 17 miles to match the ant's performance.

No one knows how many kinds of ants there are in the world. A recently published book says there are four thousand species. Another says six thousand. Edward O. Wilson (1963), who has made many scientific studies of ants, states that there are over ten thousand species.

Most of these have only scientific names simply because the average person is unaware of their existence. Without technical training most people are unable to distinguish different species of ants.

From reading and world-wide travel, however, many people now know about certain groups of ants, mainly because of what the ants do. Almost without exception, my friends who return from southern Mexico, Central America, and Venezuela tell me about the endless streams of parasol or leaf-cutting ants they have seen.

Most tourists in the western states see the large mounds of the harvester ant *Pogonomyrmex occidentalis,* and some of them know that these ants collect seeds. Few of them know there are some thirty species of *Pogonomyrmex,* or that other genera of ants also collect seeds.

Honey ants, or honey hoarders, are found in the deserts of South America, Mexico, Australia, and Africa. The one best known in the United States probably is *Myrmecocystus mexicanus hortideorum,* which is publicized as a tourist attraction in the Garden of the Gods in Colorado. These ants are relatively rare. Luckily, few people have the energy, or obtain permission, to dig them up.

The common names of ants frequently are descriptive and give some indication of the different kinds of ants. But common names are not often useful in ant identification. The red ant could be one of dozens of species, depending on the locality—Vermont, Florida, Texas, or California. The same difficulty applies to such names as meadow ants, desert ants, aphid tenders, and wood ants.

Some wood ants, such as *Formica rufa,* live in forests. Ants that excavate tunnels in wood might more properly be called wood ants. Instead,

A carpenter ant tunnel in a wood post.

they are called carpenter ants and belong to the genus *Camponotus,* which has numerous species.

George and Jeanette Wheeler have pointed out that some pest ants have been given names such as the thief ant, the cornfield ant, the odorous house ant, and the big-headed ant. People in the southern states are well acquainted with the fire ant. A list of all the kinds of ants, including driver ants, army ants, slave-making ants, and honey ants, would be endless. But such a list, without scientific names, would not tell exactly which ant was which.

Since there are so many kinds of ants, since they are almost everywhere, and since we all have dealings with them, even casual study of their social activities can give one no end of pleasure and knowledge of nature. The place for study is where you live. The method is to observe them throughout the seasons.

Most of my observations of ants have been made in Nebraska, Colorado, and Oregon where the winters are cold and the summers are warm. The seasonal cycles of these ants are different from those of warmer regions and of the tropics where ant activities continue the year around.

In our latitudes, ants become active in spring. Nest repairs are first in order. The queens of some species resume egg laying. Food collecting by the workers increases. The three stages of metamorphosis—egg, larva, pupa—result in production of adult ants. Some kinds of ants produce winged males and females that fly in spring. Others perform the marriage flight in summer and some in autumn.

Summer is the time of greatest activity for most kinds of ants. But August heat may make them retire to the moist coolness of the soil.

September and October are periods of declining activity, although some ants make their greatest food harvest at this time. As the temperature drops in late autumn the ants become sluggish and retire to the chambers of their nests for winter hibernation. Unlike honeybees, they generate no muscular heat, nor do they eat food even when they are well below the frozen soil.

Spring

SPRING, IN THE ANT WORLD, starts in small places. To the ants, the miniature climates that prevail around their nests are more important than the cold of winter that still lingers above the ground in forests, prairies, or on mountainsides. In northern localities the ants have hibernated deep in the ground, in logs in the forest and beneath stones that collect heat in the spring from the northward-marching sun.

Some ants begin their seasonal activities when the pasque flowers, dogtooth violets, anemones, and skunk cabbages appear. Some, like the little *Prenolepis imparis,* which frequently lives in apple orchards in the Midwest, actually have not strictly hibernated but have foraged during the winter whenever the soil surface temperature was above freezing.

These little ants have to hurry into their annual cycles, since the males and females that have been in the nest from the previous autumn perform their marriage flights early in April. Food finding in early spring is not a problem for them, since some of their workers have stored in

An ant apartment house built of soil.

their crops the sweet juice collected from apples that fell in October.

The big harvester ants, *Pogonomyrmex occidentalis,* of the western prairies and sagebrush deserts, begin work early as the sun's heat mounts in their foot-high gravel mounds. Since their broods of larvae and pupae will develop in the chambers and galleries of these mounds, their first job of spring is to repair the damage done in winter. I have seen this repair work begin as early as March 9 on the high plains in eastern Colorado.

The still larger carpenter ants, *Camponotus herculeanus,* which bore into logs, stumps, and dead trees, begin work with the earliest warmth of spring. On the south side of Mount Hood in Oregon I have seen them emerging from the south sides of hollow Douglas fir trees while the surrounding snow was six feet deep.

Part of their activity includes a search for insects that have died during the winter. Sometimes they congregate on the resin that exudes from scars on tree trunks where porcupines have gnawed the bark. Inside the nest, there is much activity. A faint rustling in large logs, and sometimes in walls and woodwork of houses, can be heard as the large winged males and queens prepare to emerge and establish new colonies. Queens can be seen crawling almost anywhere in wooded country in April and May.

The tiny grease ants, *Monomorium minimum,* which many people see as black lines wandering up trees, in fields, and in kitchens, sometimes migrate from greenhouses and homes to open spaces in spring. They find the warmth of dwellings suitable for existence through the cold winters of our northern climates.

Spring is a time of great activity for ants in our southern deserts. The environment of desert ants is one of extremes of cold and heat. Paradoxically, many ants that live in these habitats cannot tolerate high and low temperatures, so they dig deep formicaries to escape surface temperature extremes and work most actively above ground in spring and fall during the longest daily periods of moderate temperatures.

Lloyd Tevis found that the harvester ant *Veromessor pergandei,* which

The author excavated the underground portion of this stump to expose carpenter ant holes.

lives in Death Valley, California, in Arizona, and in the hot deserts of Mexico, is incapable of activity at temperatures below 40 degrees F. At 90 degrees F. these ants run across the sand at eight feet per minute. Temperatures above 120 degrees kill them in a few seconds. Consequently, they hunt for seeds only during the most favorable hours of the day and in spring and fall, when favorable temperatures last for several hours.

The increasing warmth of spring has a subtle influence on population growth in ant colonies. M. V. Brian found that the larvae of *Myrmica* are activated to growth by temperatures of about 44 to 47 degrees F. The queens respond by laying eggs at temperatures of about 48 to 52 degrees F. Still higher temperatures are necessary for the metamorphosis of larvae to pupae.

Later in spring, and in summer, the process of egg laying, larval development, and maturing of adult ants may be controlled by food abundance and internal factors in the physiological cycle of the colony. In tropical forests the cycle of egg laying, growth of the young, and maturing of workers is repeated every few weeks and is interrupted only by the dry season and the wet season.

In the Pacific Northwest, where I live, ants appear in increasing numbers with the advance of spring. But long before they appear in the open they are active in their nests.

A little colony of the seldom-seen *Aphaenogaster subterranea occidentalis* lives under the stones by our front doorstep. Seldom do more than two appear above ground at the same time. Mostly they remain in the dark recesses of their nest. The date of their first appearance is an event to be recorded.

I saw the first one last year on the third of April. I reported it to my family. They reacted in the same manner as John Kieran's family did when, as a boy, he enthusiastically described the "broken wing" defense of a grouse he had seen; they took it calmly.

In our back yard a colony of small reddish carpenter ants nests during

Carpenter ant winged queens and cocoons.

the summer in a piece of wood from a cherry tree that blew down in the famous Columbus Day storm. The ants first occupied the log in 1964 when the heartwood began to soften. In winter they live in galleries that extend underground beneath an adjoining stone wall. Beginning in January, I occasionally lift the block of wood and examine its underside. In 1967, I found the ants returning to their "summer" home on February 28. The temperature had previously risen above 50 degrees F. several times.

The increasingly frequent appearances of ants outside their nests in spring are harbingers of many activities to come. Food gathering begins. Nest repair and cleaning goes on apace. The queens of some species resume egg laying, and the workers busy themselves with many tasks, including care of the eggs and feeding the larvae. The older pupae turn into ants. New kings and queens spread their sphere of influence by departing on marriage flights. Always, the nest is the nucleus for all these activities.

40

Small red carpenter ants made these galleries in a cherry stump in the author's back yard.

Ants build a bewildering variety of nests. They are capable of modifying the architecture of their homes to suit the surroundings and to make use of the materials at hand. Some ants even build different kinds of nests at different periods in the colony life cycle. Owing to this plasticity of behavior it is impossible to classify and identify most kinds of ants by their nesting habits.

Some ants do not build nests. Army ants, at the end of a march, bivouac in a nest made of their own bodies. They link themselves together in chains that hang from a log or overhanging rock. As more ants join in they fuse the chains into a sleeve and finally into a living structure somewhat like a bee swarm, with the queen, the brood, and a few "camp follower" beetles snug inside for the night.

A great variety of ants nest in plant cavities or among living plant

These galleries were made by harvester ants.

parts. Some excavate their own cavities. Others prefer ready-made cavities—they live in prefabricated houses.

The little *Leptothorax curvispinosus*, which is found from New England west to Iowa and Missouri and south to the Gulf Coast, nests in hollow acorns and stems lying on the ground. Other ants live in galls, seed pods, and in the crevices between bark and wood.

In the tropics, such a multitude of ants live in hollow stems, hollow thorns, hollow bulbs, and in nests suspended in trees that Willian Morton Wheeler wrote a book about them under the title *Studies of Neotropical Ant Plants and Their Ants.*

The ants that live in hollow branches of cecropia trees in South America have been known for more than three hundred years. The ants cut holes through the partitions in the trunk and branches so they have protected runways to all parts of the tree. These ants produce large

42

colonies and protect their trees against all comers, including other species of ants.

The hollow thorns of the bull-horn acacia in tropical America are among the most remarkable of ant nests. *Pseudomyrma* ants bore holes in these thorns, which resemble in shape the horns of a bull, and there raise their families. These ants save the acacia trees from leaf-cutting ants *(Atta),* which are capable of removing the leaves from an entire tree overnight.

Among the ants that dwell in twigs and plant galls, those of the subgenus *Colobopsis* have a most unusual method of excluding intruders. The heads of the queen and the major workers are nearly cylindrical and of just the right size to fit the one circular opening to the nest. The worker uses her head as a door and withdraws it only when stroked on the face by the antennae of the minor workers who wish to enter. These ants are abundant in the southern states and nest in twigs of hickory, pecan, and ash trees and in the hollow stems of weeds.

There are ants that nest in peat moss and ants that live in the tillandsias that festoon the trees in Florida and the Gulf states. Many ants live in nests, suspended in trees, which are made of material similar to the paper in a wasp's nest. Certain South American ants construct tree nests of earth and then plant flower seeds in the soil so the resulting vegetation will protect the nest from rain.

The most fabulous accomplishment in nest building is that in which worker ants combine forces to pull the edges of leaves together while other workers hold their own larvae in their mandibles and apply the spinning organs of the larvae to the leaves. Literally, they use their babies to sew their nest together with silk. These ants live in Asia.

Ants of the temperate climate, with which most of us are familiar, make nests in dead wood or in the soil. Frequently there is no crater or mound of earth to mark the location of the nest. The soil particles that compose the little craters of earth brought up by garden ants and by many of the meadow ants soon are dispersed by wind, animals, or rain.

Ants build many kinds of nests. This is a crater nest.

The tiny craters made by dooryard ants are often washed away by rain.

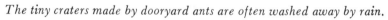

Spring

The real nest is underground, and if you wish to see its architecture you must dig carefully. Mary Talbot, in studying the populations of *Prenolepis imparis,* had laborers first dig a hole large enough for a person to stand in near the entrance to the nest. Then with three to five hours of careful excavation, beginning at the ground surface, she mapped on cross-section paper the location of the chambers and galleries of the nest. White ink squirted periodically in the nest helped her trace the galleries.

My digging has been mostly with the much larger harvester ant, *Pogonomyrmex occidentalis,* in eastern Colorado, Utah, and Oregon. The mounds of these ants sometimes reach a height of 18 inches and a basal diameter of 2 to 5 feet. In spring, summer, and fall these mounds are used for seed storage and for all the reproductive activities of the ants.

In volcanic country in Idaho and Oregon the ants make their mounds of lava particles. In desert areas they use sand grains. Sometimes they add sagebrush twigs. In the Red Desert of Wyoming they bring up small rubies from below ground. These can be seen shining red in the sunlight.

In eastern Oregon, at the edge of U. S. Highway 30, I found a harvester ant mound covered with green and brown glass fragments from shattered bottles. The harvester ants near Grand Junction, Colorado, use petrified shark teeth that have remained in conglomerate since the Cretaceous period of the Mesozoic era. Near Lander, Wyoming, the harvester ants sometimes surface their mounds with a combination of sand and particles of green jade.

Excavation of a harvester ant nest can be a Herculean task. The galleries extend downward ten feet or more in a cone-shaped area. In summer, when the ants are extremely active, the digging job may be precarious since the ants can bite and sting viciously.

In excavating the colonies of large biting ants I have found it expedient to pour a jigger of commercial chloroform into each of several holes punched in the top of the mound. The chloroform vapor sinks through the galleries and immobilizes most of the ants. This is especially helpful in photography of mound and colony structure, since the ants do not immediately carry off all the larvae, pupae, and seeds.

One of the most extensive ant nest excavations I know of is the one reported by John C. Moser on a large nest of the town ant, *Atta texana*, in central Louisiana in 1960. This fungus-culturing ant, also known as the Texas leaf-cutting ant, causes serious damage to crops and trees in Louisiana and east Texas.

The moderately large nest covered an area of about 35 by 50 feet. A bulldozer was used to cut a swath about 7½ feet wide and 100 feet long through the nest. Moser states, "The bottom of the nest was not reached, as vertical galleries were still found at a level of 12 feet, where excavation was halted for fear that the sides of the cut would collapse."

In western Colorado, fossil shark teeth, averaging a quarter-inch in length, are used by harvester ants to build mounds.

Scale model of underground chambers in a town ant nest. A man could crawl into the largest chamber of the actual nest. (John C. Moser)

The excavation uncovered ninety-three fungus gardens, of which fifty-two contained some fungus, and, of course, many ants. Fungus garden cavities are dome-shaped and average a foot in diameter, but occasionally one is large enough to hold a man.

Some of these nests are so huge that the underground portion may occupy more than five acres. On the surface, well-defined trails extend a hundred feet or more beyond so-called "feeder holes" to trees or other plants that are being stripped of leaves.

Probably the nests most exasperating to people are those made by fire ants, which were imported from South America and have invaded most of the southern states. The mound above the nest is a honeycombed structure of earth which may be 30 inches in diameter and 24 inches in height. These mounds become as hard as rocks and create special problems in parks, on lawns, and in pastures, where they break mower blades when hay is being cut.

47

Fungus garden made by town ants in Louisiana. (John C. Moser)

Some of the large *Formica* ants build fabulous mounds of twigs, pine or fir needles, and other debris. These ants, which are protected by foresters in Germany because of their insect control habits, have been known to build nests 4 feet high and 10 feet in diameter. The largest nest I have ever seen in Oregon was 34 inches high and 78 inches wide at the base.

These large nests are well insulated from moisture and temperature changes by the thatching material. Sometimes a pit is excavated 12 to 16 inches deep below the surface portion of the nest. This pit also is filled with insulating material, especially dry evergreen needles and portions of dried leaves. Here the queen and her colony stay in cold weather. The nests I have examined in winter have had temperatures above freezing even though the ground outside was covered with snow.

If you are looking for ant nests almost anywhere in the United States, try turning flat stones. Beneath you are quite likely to find *Lasius niger* or one of the species of that genus. These so-called garden ants are among

48

the commonest ants in North America. As the stone is turned you will have to look quickly, for the larvae and pupae will be rushed into the underground tunnels. If you dig carefully, somewhere in the nest you may find the queen. She will be much larger than the rest of the ants.

Sudden damage to an ant nest always results first in rescue of the young. Some ants attack the aggressor, or the cause of the disturbance, if it can be found. Some of the small, timid species of ants do not attack but simply vanish into hiding places. When the danger is past, nest repair begins.

The repair of large nests may take many days or even weeks. The thatching ants I have observed first fill in the hole with material from the demolished nest and from the surrounding territory. Then they remodel the internal architecture, connecting new galleries with old ones and making new chambers for the inhabitants.

Severe damage to a large harvester ant nest may require a whole summer for repair, since they have to collect much of the gravel for

Fire ant mounds in a southern pasture. These mounds are almost as hard as rocks. (U. S. Forest Service)

their mound from many yards beyond the nest. Only a small portion of the gravel is brought up from below ground. The job of cementing the new roof to make it waterproof and smoothing the vaulted ceilings and walls of the galleries requires much time.

The harvester ants in the West have another annual repair job that starts in the spring. One of their first activities is the removal of new vegetation from the large bare circles that surround their mounds. Clearing is well under way by May 15 in Oregon and Utah.

The ants climb the young plants, sometimes twenty or thirty ants at a time, and remove the leaves with their mandibles. Then they cut off small branches and finally in piecemeal fashion remove the stems until only stubs remain above ground. The material removed is dropped, carried to the edge of the clearing, or blown away by the wind.

These cleared areas, which may be from 10 to 50 feet in diameter, dry rapidly after rainstorms and thus possibly prevent molding and sprouting of seeds stored below ground near the periphery of the ant nest. Rain

A Formica *ant nest. Aphids that produce honeydew for the ants are found on the nearby fir trees.*

This Formica *ant city contained an estimated third of a million ants.*

water usually drains to the edge of the clearing, where it promotes luxuriant growth of weeds and grasses such as tansy mustard, downy brome grass, gumweed, and prairie sunflowers. These plants form an excellent windbreak, which is effective in the area where the ants work.

I believe these cleared circles have protected the harvester ants through thousands of years of prairie fires. When a fire roars past their nests there is nothing to burn and the ground itself does not become heated to an intolerable degree.

Life in an ant nest occupied by our little dooryard ants, with maybe only a few dozen ants, is simple when compared to the multitude of activities that occur in the vicinity of a harvester ant mound or a wood

51

Nest detail showing Formica fusca *workers, worker cocoons, and queen cocoons.*

These Formica *cocoons, as well as eggs and larvae, are placed in nest chambers without benefit of bedding material.*

ant nest with its suburbs and vast hinterlands where thousands of ants pasture their aphid cows and hunt for meat for the community larder.

Derek Wragge Morley, who studied the whole history of British wood ants, found that a large ant city contained half a million ants. As in any city with this many inhabitants, there is great division of labor. As many as sixty queens keep busy laying eggs. Ten thousand nurses care for the queens and their broods. The eggs have to be licked and the grubs have to be fed. Twenty to thirty thousand workers are engaged in food collection. Repairs and alterations to the nest require one hundred thousand ant days of labor per day. Since one third of the population dies each year and five hundred deaths occur each day, twenty-four hundred days of laboring time are spent removing the dead alone.

The multitudinous tasks performed in an ant city of this size are fantastic. Some twenty-five thousand grubs and cocoons are moved each day to rooms with favorable temperatures. The young grubs, recently hatched from eggs, are placed in chambers near the queens. As they grow, they are moved to chambers near the entrances to the mound where they receive food from incoming workers.

This loose pile of soil particles conceals the underground nest of the Lasius.

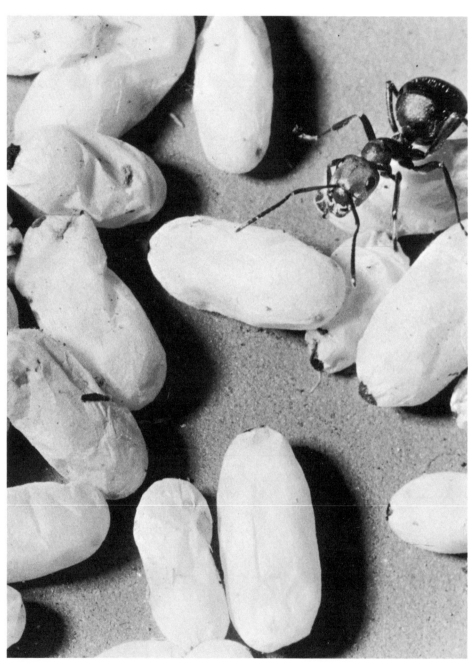

A thatching ant guarding cocoons.

Spring

When the larvae have spun their cocoons, they are moved like baggage to other rooms. When they show signs of movement within the cocoons, the worker ants act as midwives and assist at the "birth" of the new ants.

In the daily routine of the nest, the gates of the city are opened in the morning and closed in the evening. Friends and foes are identified. Drainage passages in the ground are patrolled and cleaned.

Outside, trails are constructed to smaller nests in the suburbs, which are a part of the metropolitan area. If, as I once observed on the Starkey Experimental Forest and Range in eastern Oregon, the mother nest is burned, the queens in one or more of the outlying towns can start a new city. This rejuvenation of the community may require five years or more.

In the hinterlands, food-collecting ants follow trails to trees and shrubs where they tend aphids for their sweet excreta or collect honeydew from galls. Others hunt for insects, worms, and other kinds of meat in the grass jungles far from home.

On the return journey they converge and follow trails that are veritable Appian Ways. On one of these highways in the Blue Mountains I counted an average of 316 ants passing a given point every minute. The outgoing ants were traveling light. The incoming ants were arriving with gasters swollen with liquid food or with mandibles clutching insects, caterpillars, and material for building the nest.

In all these marvelous labors, the ants were making use of their senses of smell, sight, and touch. The various castes of ants were producing different odorous compounds, and these odors were fundamental to the social behavior and the daily labor in the ant city.

In some ants, these odors originate in the head in the reservoir of the mandibular gland. *Lasius neoniger* males, for example, produce odors that may serve as sex pheromones or attractants for winged queens.

The minor workers of *Pheidole fallax* lay odor trails with volatile substances produced by Dufour's gland, which is located in the abdomens of the ants. Other ants produce odors that are recognition compounds and serve to distinguish a given species from all other species.

55

Formica ants, crawling out of a honey jar, walk over one another without objection.

Most of the communication among ants is chemical. Recognition of chemical odors is made principally through the antennae. If the antennae are cut off or are covered with varnish, ants may attack their own nest mates or walk peacefully among enemies.

The antennae not only are highly sensitive to odors but also to touch and to size and shape of objects. The use of antennal communication by army ants, *Eciton hamatum,* was observed by Dr. William M. Mann (1948). When he removed a few ants from the line of march, those nearest the disturbance turned back and touched antennae to all followers. Instantly the army began retracing its steps.

Ants apparently find their way not only by odor but by the position of the sun and by landmarks which they can see near at hand. Julian

Huxley has suggested that ants also have a kinesthetic sense, or "muscular memory." The amount of exertion, or the number of leg movements, is somehow registered so the ant knows how far it has traveled.

A number of ants make sounds. Leaf-cutting ants *(Atta)* squeak if they are held fast. It is not known if this signal brings rescue crews to release them from the confinement of a cave-in of their tunnels. Ross E. Hutchins states that some ants make tapping sounds and that a Brazilian carpenter ant emits a whirring sound.

Hayward G. Spangler reports that harvester ants *Pogonomyrmex occidentalis* can alternate the chirp intensity and interrupt chirps into distinct pulses. The stridulations are produced by moving the abdomen up and down so that a scraper on the petiole rubs on a filelike area on the gaster. The meanings of these messages, sent by vibrations through the substrate, are not understood at present.

Sight is not acute in ants; indeed, some ants are totally blind. But others with large compound eyes, such as workers and soldiers of *Atta,* will respond to the waving of a finger within an inch of their heads. My wood ants in their glass cage respond readily to the wave of my hand, especially when it alters the intensity of light in their nest.

Edward O. Wilson, in his study of behavior of the Neotropical ant, *Daceton armigerum,* states that "Foraging workers in the field clearly were very perceptive visually to movement. They wheeled quickly to face any moving object. If the object was a large one, such as a human hand, the ants darted in reverse, revealing the curious ability to run backward as rapidly as forward. Slight movement, which must be close to the ant, induced a cautious movement toward the object."

Some ants that travel a great deal in the open are able to orient themselves by polarized light, which we humans cannot see. The ants travel not only toward or away from the light stimulus but are able to move at an angle to the source of the light and to compensate for the movement of the sun. I have done this many times in the woods with visible light, allowing for the change in direction of shadows of trees. But the

The mandibles, or "jaws," of a thatching ant require strong muscles.

ants can do it even when the sun is invisible since they are sensitive to the plane of polarization from the sky.

Wherever an ant may be, its mandibles or "jaws" are always ready to do whatever work is needed. Few of us realize that, without mandibles, ants and their works could not exist.

Mandibles appear in many shapes and forms. Some are shovel shaped and, when closed, form a kind of trowel for raking up earth and molding and compressing materials into nests.

Many times I have watched this process carefully with a magnifying glass while some of my soil-inhabiting ants dug galleries in their glass cage. Like gold miners they dug "stopes," or overhead excavations, by clawing almost straight up with their front legs and producing a shower of fine particles. When a large stone was encountered, the ant carried it to the end of the tunnel and with its mandibles actually pushed the stone into place, making the soil particles move behind the stone. I believe this is one reason for the nest structure holding so tightly in dry soil.

The mandibles, which open sideways, are like a pair of tongs with toothed edges. They are used for fighting, cutting up prey, excavating soil or wood, and transporting their eggs, their young, and one another.

Ants do not chew food with their mandibles; adult ants ingest only liquid food. The solid pieces of insects, plant parts, and particles of fruits are packed into a pocket under the mouth cavity where the juices are squeezed out and swallowed. The remaining pellet of solid material is discarded. Saliva is used to moisten sugar, starch, and other foods.

The food of ants comes from many sources. Except for the specialized ants that eat only fungus hyphae or rely mainly on seeds or honeydew secreted by aphids, mealy bugs, and tree hoppers, ants as a group are unbiased in their choice of food, especially if it is the meat of arthropods such as spiders, centipedes, and insects. Some ants eat other ants. And in times of food shortage they may eat their own eggs and brood.

In early spring, ant food may be scarce. The first food collection by ground-dwelling and wood-dwelling ants generally is directed toward insects that have lived through the winter in sheltered spots. Insect bodies and parts of insects also are sought since they are good sources of protein, which is needed in colonies where the young ant broods develop early.

The honey ants, which have stored in their bodies the sweet secretions from plants and fruits during the previous season, have their spring supply of food readily available through regurgitation.

In cold countries the little Pharaoh's ant, *Monomorium pharaonis,* which embarked on ships from Egypt and spread over the entire world, lives in houses. It enjoys a catholic diet of sugar, pastry, butter, bread, lard, cheese, meat, or whatever other food its human hosts leave unprotected.

The fire ants, *Solenopsis saevissima,* of the South are equally capable of feeding themselves in spring because of their nondiscriminating appetites. In the fields they sometimes feed on young cabbage, okra, eggplant, and germinating seed corn. Damage to plants in general, however,

Dead butterflies are a favorite ant food, including the wings.

Cornfield ants place their aphids underground on the roots of corn plants.

is rare. It has been said that they are fond of young quail and enter the pipped eggs to get them. They chase brooding hens off their nests and eat their chicks. Fire ants devour housefly larvae, boll weevil grubs, cutworms, and other destructive insects and thus have their beneficial qualities.

Many of the "dairy-farming" ants, which use the honey of aphids for food, store the aphid eggs and adults in underground tunnels until spring. Some ants place the adult aphids on grass roots below ground until spring is assured and it is safe to transplant their "cows" to other kinds of plants.

The cornfield ant, *Lasius niger americanus,* transfers its aphids to the roots of young corn plants in mid-spring. The aphids reproduce so rapidly that by midsummer they kill many of the corn plants.

The little meadow ant *Solenopsis fugax* builds its galleries in the nests

61

of other ants. From its tunnels, which are too small to admit its victims, it dashes out and steals the brood and provisions of its larger neighbors.

Many of the hunting ants explore their foraging areas singly, examining foliage and crevices with their antennae. The tree-dwelling ant *Daceton armigerum* actually stalks and chases its insect prey, which it can see if the distance is less than a centimeter. The mandibular strike is quick and decisive, the sharp apical teeth being driven deeply into the body of the insect prey.

The driver ants of Africa and the army ants of South America advance in battalions, flushing out all kinds of prey, including tarantulas, scorpions, grasshoppers, snakes, lizards, and small mammals. The prey is overpowered by the sheer force of numbers of biting ants.

The large black ants of the *Formica fusca* group hunt singly in every direction for many yards around their masonry domed nests in our Pacific Northwest woods. Several years ago in the pine-fir woods of eastern Washington, I found these ants so numerous that one or more was present on every grass blade. They were collecting Pacific grass bugs, *Irbisia pacifica,* which suck the juice from plants valuable for cattle forage.

This ant city uses a stump for anchorage. Aphids on the trees provide food.

Spring

The wandering ability of harvester ants is notable. Like the insect-hunting ants, they forage singly and seemingly at random, since they are searching for seeds. The ants from a large colony are capable of covering almost every square inch of ground daily within a radius of fifty feet of their nest.

Many of our smaller ants wander singly in search of food, and when it is found they lay an odor trail back to the nest. Soon this trail is followed by other workers to the source of food.

Large more or less permanent foraging trails are constructed by ants that travel from the nest to a relatively stationary source of food. The *Formica* ants that tend aphids on fir trees in the Rocky Mountains frequently have trails through grass an inch wide and more than a hundred feet long. Beyond that, the trail may extend nearly a hundred feet up the trunk of a large tree and then branch out to the needles where the aphids are feeding.

Leaf-cutting ants sometimes make foraging trails that are six inches wide near the nest and are hundreds of feet long. These paths are kept clear of all vegetation. On the other hand, some of the tiny ants, such as those that dwell in acorns, are stay-at-home people. They travel only a few feet from their nests. The entire world of the thorn-dwelling ants may be the acacia trees in which they live.

M. J. Way, on the other hand, has found that ants from colonies of *Oecophylla longinoda* range over a thousand feet from their nests in coconut plantations in Zanzibar. Colonies of army ants in the Congo cover as much as ten to twelve acres.

The harvester ants of the West travel extensively as spring advances. I have found them carrying wheat grains dropped from trucks on roads more than two hundred feet distant from the nest.

The changes in ant travels and other activities in late spring are legion. With the increasing heat of summer, some ants go into a form of hibernation, or estivation. The harvesters become more active, since their favorite seeds from spring annuals have dried and disseminated. The

Formica *ants tending aphids on a Douglas fir branch in eastern Oregon.*

aphid-tending ants are just coming into their greatest activity, since several generations have multiplied their "cows" to fantastic numbers. The insect hordes of early summer have begun to appear, and so the meat-eating ants have good hunting.

Summer

SUMMER IS THE BUSY TIME of the year for ants. Food supplies of honey-dew, nectar, insects, flower petals, and seeds are at their peak. The luxuriant growth of foliage protects the ants from bird and animal predators. The heat of day, warmth of night, and the soil-softening effect of occasional rains provide, at one time or another, periods suitable for colony activities of most of our native ants.

Ants find food collecting easy in summer. The constant stream of edible material that flows into the nest provides energy for work and for multiplication of ant numbers through increased egg laying, larval and pupal growth, and formation of males and queens.

The mating queens find congenial weather for the flights that dissem-inate the species. When they come to earth, the soil or other substratum

Sunflowers and many other plants provide food for aphids, which in turn provide food for ants.

generally is in condition for digging and establishment of the new colony.

If you wish to study ants closely, they can be found almost anywhere in summer. Recently, I stopped in the sagebrush desert twenty miles west of Squaw Butte, Oregon, to see what ants were there. A harvester ant mound was easily visible from the road. Within three feet of this mound I found the twig-covered nest of *Formica* ants and a stone-covered nest of the little *Lasius niger,* which is common throughout much of the northern United States.

The harvester ants were collecting brome grass seeds. The thatching ants were gathering dead insects, including small beetles and leaf hoppers. The *Lasius* ants were tending hundreds of aphids on the leaves of a sagebrush plant above their nest. The three kinds of ants did not seem to be interfering with one another.

Rotting stumps and logs in shaded woodlands are fruitful sources for finding ants. Mary Talbot, who studied ants in the sand dunes on the south shore of Lake Michigan many years ago, unknowingly sparked my interest in log successions and their insect populations. When a tree dies, *Leptothorax* ants may first use the crevices in the bark for their nests. Other stages of decay follow: the bark loosens, the sapwood

Aphids tended by ants on sagebrush.

Carpenter ants on a log. The sawdust comes from the hole they made.

becomes soft, the heartwood decays, the log loses its shape, and finally, after many years, the substance of the wood merges with the soil. In each of these stages, characteristic ants live for a time and then give way to other species.

In studying ants I have often found myself acting like a bear, turning over small logs or tearing them apart whenever I am in the woods. However, in order to expose carpenter ants in the big logs of the Pacific Northwest, I have found it necessary to use a chain saw, a maul, and a set of steel wedges. *Camponotus herculeanus,* the big carpenter ant, lives in solid wood!

Carpenter ants seem impelled to drop the sawdust from their doorways into thin air. One nest that I observed for several years near LaGrande, Oregon, had two openings in the base of a dead larch tree. The first opening was about two feet above the ground. On warm summer days an ant would thrust its head out of the doorway about every ten seconds, open its mandibles, and let fall its particle of sawdust.

The second doorway opened on top of a slanting root where the sawdust could not be dropped without eventually burying the entrance. The ants invariably came out in the open, walked to the edge of the

Carpenter ant, with a particle of sawdust in its mandibles, prepares to cast it on the growing pile.

root, and cast their sawdust over the edge. By so doing, they exposed themselves to birds and other enemies, but they avoided the accumulation of a trash pile in front of their doorway.

Ant nests and cities vary enormously in their complexity of structure and in the activities of their ants. The little ants in our dooryards build only a vertical tunnel with a few side rooms for the queen and her brood. The nest may last for only a few months.

The leaf-cutting ants of our southern states build nests marked by great numbers of crescent-shaped mounds a foot or more in diameter and several inches in height. Each of these mounds surrounds an entrance hole. The holes lead to innumerable cavities that are connected by tunnels. Since a single large underground nest is marked by many mounds, these ants, *Atta texana*, are sometimes called town ants.

In recent years, scientists have become interested in the study of labor productivity and efficiency in large colonies of ants. Edward O. Wilson reports that a study of earth moving by British ants showed that *"Lasius flavus* colonies, while occupying average areas of about 50 square yards, used about 330 g of earth per year in nest building."

Wilson also reports that S. J. Holt, "In an analysis of foraging activity of a mature *Formica rufa* Linnaeus colony, calculated that on one typical day, 60 to 70 thousand workers, weighing 700 g, made 300 thousand foraging trips to collect at least 800 g of food, of which 44 per cent was honeydew." In laboratory studies, R. Stumper estimated that *Proformica nasuta* ants doled out honeydew, stored in their crops, to sister workers at the estimated energy rate of 0.04 calories per worker day. At this rate, a colony of seventy thousand ants would require about the same amount of energy as a human being using 2,800 calories per day.

Recently, I attempted to estimate the amount of work done by harvester ants near Burns, Oregon. In an area where the mounds averaged approximately fifty per acre, I weighed ten typical mounds and found that the earth and gravel averaged 159 pounds per mound, or nearly four tons per acre.

An amazing aspect of this ability of harvester ants to do work was the weight of the ants themselves. My friend George A. Garrison, using a sensitive balance, determined the dry body weights of nineteen of these ants and found that they varied from .0041 to .0152 grams. The average

Carpenter ants have dropped a quart of sawdust, piece by piece, from the hole near the author's left hand.

was .0086 grams. The average ant leg weighed .00065 grams.

Harvester ants and many desert ants that excavate large quantities of soil are provided with a basket, or *"psammophore,"* which consists of rows of long curved hairs beneath the lower surface of the head. Some scientists believe that the ants transport soil particles to the surface in small masses held by these baskets instead of wasting time carrying single grains with their mandibles.

Food gathering in summer requires much ant time and energy. In its simplest form, it involves individual activity until food is found. Some ants then lead foragers to the food source. Others lay scent trails back to the nest so that groups of ants may retrieve the food. M. V. Brian has pointed out that scouting for food by a few ants minimizes exposure of large numbers of their fellows to ant enemies and to unfavorable changes in weather.

Harvester ants do not lay scent trails or attract helpers to food sources; each ant searches alone until it finds a seed or other piece of food, which it carries home alone.

Harvester ants collect and store in their granaries the seeds of halogeton, a desert plant poisonous to sheep.

Summer

In my observations of harvester ants, I have found them collecting more than a hundred kinds of seeds, insects, and other materials. These include seeds of blue grama, western wheatgrass, three-awn grass, cheatgrass, tumbling mustard, rubber rabbitbrush, pigweeds, lamb's-quarters, sunflowers, peppergrass, Russian thistle, silky sophora, solitary bees, grasshoppers, beetles, berries, and bird dung.

Entrance to the nests or formicaries is by one or two gates which may be at the base or part way up the ant hill. Usually, a vestibule from one to two inches wide and about three fourths of an inch high is found just inside the gate. From this foyer, tubular galleries connect with the granaries and nurseries in the mound and deep in the ground.

The granaries or storerooms are circular, oval, crescent-shaped, or horseshoe-shaped and have diameters of one to four inches and heights up to one inch. In summer, many of the storerooms are only one or two inches below the surface.

Henry C. McCook, in his book, *The Agricultural Ant of Texas,* published in 1879, described the granaries of *Pogonomyrmex barbatus:*

In the upper ones the larger part of the seeds were still within the shell, the most of those in the lower rooms being husked, and some of them quite green. Green and dry seeds were found together in granaries fifteen inches from the top. The seeds were piled up one upon another, apparently nearly to the roof. Narrow gangways were left at the outer margin between the grain-heaps and the wall. . . . From these store-rooms fully a pint of seeds, chiefly of buffalo-grass, was taken, the greater amount being in the galleries nearest the surface. The greatest depth at which seeds were found was two and a half feet.

In a recent study of the harvester ant *Pogonomyrmex owyheei,* near Redmond, Oregon, J. R. Willard and H. H. Crowell used cracked grain colored green, blue, red, yellow, and white with vegetable dye to test the ants' foraging ability. Mounds were ringed at different distances with one-half gallon of cracked grain and excavated twenty-four hours later. The average amount of grain recovered from each mound aver-

71

aged one-fifth quart. This same study "showed that ants from colonies 40 ft. or less apart definitely overlap in their foraging, and in some cases the ants from one colony foraged to the base of the mound of another colony."

Harvester ants chew seeds and rasp the starch with their tongues. While chewing they add saliva, which changes the starch to sugar. The ant bread that results may be eaten or it may be stored temporarily in the granaries.

The husks of grains that have been "threshed" are taken outside where they are blown away by the wind. Seeds that sprout in the vicinity of the nest are those lost by the ants or blown in by the wind. Seeds are not deliberately planted by the ants.

Not all harvesting ants belong to the genus *Pogonomyrmex*. The old-world harvesters of King Solomon, Virgil, and other ancient writers belong to the genus *Messor*. In Arizona there is a harvesting ant, *Pheidole militicida*, which has large soldier forms that protect their colonies against raids by other ants.

Some scientists have speculated that, in ages past, ants that now cultivate fungus gardens originally may have been seed collectors. Molds and other fungi are likely to grow on the compost materials in damp chambers of ant nests. And it is well known that town ants, parasol ants, and others carefully weed their gardens of all but desirable fungi. Hence, it has been suggested that seed-collecting ants, while weeding their gran-

Ants entering their nest in a ponderosa pine log.

aries, may have acquired a taste for fungi and the ability to cultivate them.

Certainly the ants are expert gardeners. Each species grows its own fungus. But not all of these types of ants use leaves for compost. One kind that lives in very small colonies uses caterpillar excrement as soil for their gardens.

Although I have seen no published report, I am inclined to believe that a number of ant species that dwell in shrubby areas and forests use mycorhizae for food. A mycorhiza is a combination of root and specific soil fungi consisting of a feltlike sheath of fungus threads that surround the root and penetrate its epidermis and cortex. The relationship is believed to be symbiotic—that is, beneficial to both the green plant and the fungus.

In the Cascade Mountains of Oregon I have excavated certain types of ant nests in the ponderosa pine zone in which the ants always seem to be associated with the roots of pine or antelope bitter brush. Invariably the micorhizae are exposed in the galleries and chambers in the ant nests. At least, the relationship appears to merit further investigation.

The complex associations between ants and aphids reach their greatest expression in summer. The many adaptations of aphid feeding and nutrition have been reviewed by Jacques Auclair. Aphids feed on the sap of leaves and plant stems by means of stylets inserted into plant tissue. The sap is converted into honeydews and mannas that are excreted by the aphids and are taken into the crops of ants and thus transported to the ant colonies.

Honeydews contain sugars—dextrins, fructose, glucose, sucrose—free amino acids, phosphates, citric acid, and other acids but apparently are lacking in proteins. Hence the ants, in order to obtain a balanced diet, eat other insects, including their own aphid cows.

Ants "milk" their aphids by stroking them with their antennae. This causes the aphid to exude a small drop of honeydew, which is lapped up by the ant.

Grasshoppers and countless other insects provide ants with needed protein.

Ants move their aphids from place to place. Sometimes they carry them to their nests at night, and they keep aphid eggs and adults in their nests in winter. The cornfield ants and many other species place aphids underground on the roots of growing plants. In some cases the ants defend the aphids against attack by other insects.

The association between ants and other insects for the benefit of each, but without complete dependence on one another, has been called "mutualism." M. J. Way, in an extensive review of mutualism, points out that many aphids can live without ants. Many ants, of course, live without aphids.

When ants are absent, most aphids produce droplets of honeydew that are ejected by contracting the abdomen or are kicked off by a hind leg. Most everyone who has parked an automobile under trees in summer has returned to find it covered with honeydew.

The larvae of some of the gossamer-winged butterflies secrete honeydew that attracts ants, and some live in ant nests. If the ants fail to remove the honeydew, the larvae become contaminated and quickly die.

There has been much discussion about the purpose of the silken and paper shelters that ants build over aphids and honeydew-producing coccids. These "cow sheds" are believed to protect the ants from battering rain and only incidentally protect the "cows."

Some aphids and other Homoptera definitely could not survive in northern winters except in ant nests. The ant *Lasius flavus,* for example, not only protects its overwintering guests against fungi, excessive moisture, and low temperatures but constantly licks the eggs to keep them from shriveling.

The honey ants *Myrmecocystus mexicanus hortideorum,* which are best known from the Garden of the Gods near Colorado Springs, Colorado, depend mainly on honeydew from oak galls that are caused by gall wasps. These ants make nightly forays to obtain the sweet watery solution exuded by the galls. This liquid is then carried in the crops of the workers and fed to storage ants or repletes until their abdomens are stretched like tiny grapes.

These animated honeypots hang from the ceilings of their underground chambers for many months and can regurgitate food for their fellow workers when it is unavailable outdoors. The abdomens of some are almost transparent. Others are amber colored. Some are almost black.

Paul W. Nesbit, who carefully guards honey ant nests in his back yard in Colorado Springs, believes that the dark-colored repletes have stored the honey so long that it has fermented. He told me that it tastes sour, whereas the clear honey from light-colored repletes tastes sweet.

Henry C. McCook, in 1882, was the first to publish a trustworthy account of the Garden of the Gods honey ants. Long before this, however, the Indians of Mexico and the southwestern states used repletes as a source of food, since several species of honey ants are widely distributed in the Southwest. The great depth of these ant nests—as much as sixteen feet—appears to be a defense against the extremes of temperature in desert climates.

For defense against living enemies, for fighting, and for food collecting, ants use bites, sprays, and stings. The mandibles of larger ants are especially adapted for biting.

Aphids on rose stem just below the bud.

Same aphids, greatly enlarged. Many aphids live without ants, and many ants live without aphids.

Honey ants, with gasters distended by honey. An ant sometimes bursts if it falls from the ceiling of its chamber. (Paul W. Nesbit)

The red bull ant, *Myrmecia gulosa,* is capable of biting a crescent-shaped piece of leather from one's shoe. In addition, it has histamine in its venom, which relates it to the venom of the honey bee.

The bites and stings of ants are independent—they bite from the front end and sting from the rear end. The fire ant of the South lifts the skin of man and animals with its mandibles, curves its abdomen under its thorax, and injects the venom. Fiery pain occurs immediately and angry welts develop on the skin.

Mrs. Robert W. Campbell, who lived in Louisiana for several years, told me that fire ants are apt to crawl above one's shoes and, on a given signal, all bite at once. Bill Cummings, who spent many months in Africa, told me that certain red ants in the jungle act in the same way. They generally attack when one is quietly observing wildlife or stalking game.

Once, and only once, I intentionally permitted a harvester ant to bite and sting the back of my left hand. The immediate pain was like the stab of a wasp. Within ten minutes an inflamed circle of skin appeared. A white spot remained in the center of the one-inch red area for more than two hours. The pain and itching subsided in one hour, but beads of perspiration appeared in the area of the sting for more than a week.

On another occasion, while digging a harvester ant nest in Idaho, I was stung on the hip by several ants that had crawled inside my clothing. I undressed in sight of all the tourists passing on U. S. Highway 30. The pain persisted for more than an hour, and my left leg and foot felt numb and cold for more than four hours.

Two deaths from harvester ant stings have been reported in Oklahoma and one from fire ants in Louisiana. It is easy to believe that the Southwestern Indians once staked their human victims on ant hills for torture.

Venoms and repellents in ants are products of exocrine, or ducted, glands. Ants have many glands: mandibular glands; salivary glands; pharyngeal glands, which have a digestive function; venom glands, in the cavity of the gaster; and anal glands, which exude defense and alarm secretions.

Many people are familiar with the formic acid odor of ants in the subfamily Formicinae. Formic acid is used to incapacitate prey and to repel intruders from the nest. While photographing *Formica rufa* ants under bright lights I have seen them squirt formic acid to a distance of three inches. Edwin Way Teale reports that a lighted candle in the nest of a wood ant colony was extinguished by a formic acid barrage.

All ants do not possess venom or formic acid. Many have other ingenious methods of defense against enemies. John C. Moser reports that possum ants, *Trachymyrmex,* which cultivate underground fungus gardens, often play dead when picked up. Harvester ants of the South sting when molested. Town ants bite. There is an African ant, *Megaloponera foetens,* that discharges a nauseating odor to repel enemies.

The most unusual passive defense I know of is the one described by Dr. William M. Mann. An ant in the Fiji Islands, with the tongue-twisting name *Rogeria stigmatica* subspecies *sublevinodis,* secretes a

Thatching ant pupae (one is emerging) and three larvae.

Harvester ant larvae and pupae from the Idaho sagebrush desert.

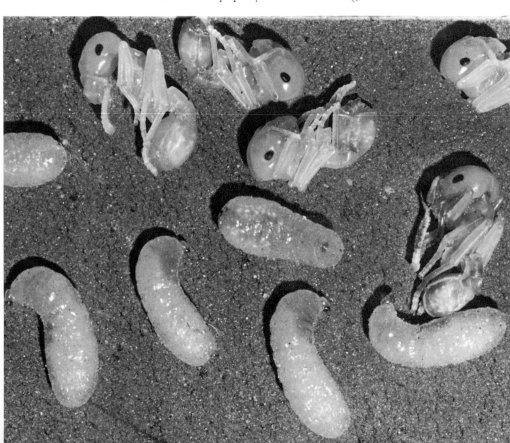

viscid substance from its anal glands in threads one half to three fourths of an inch long that resemble worms. These threads, which possibly are hygroscopic, twist in a lifelike manner while the ants, which are the color of the earth, remain motionless.

These varied defense activities tend to ensure minimum worker losses. Thus the population is maintained more easily and food is assured for the many activities that occur in the nest.

Continuation of the colony, of course, is dependent on egg laying by the queen. The queen in an established colony, however, does not care for the eggs. Instead, they are removed from her chamber and stored in rooms and hallways by nursemaids. Commonly, the nursemaids are young ants, or callows, that remain in the nest until their exoskeletons harden and assume the colors of the mature workers. Any worker, however, can take over the duties of caring for eggs, larvae, and pupae.

The eggs must be licked if they are to hatch. The larvae must be cleaned and fed. Some are fed by regurgitation. Nursemaids of the fungus-growing ants slice off the kohlrabilike tips of fungus hyphae for the larvae or, in some instances, carry the larvae to the fungus gardens where they feed themselves.

The larvae of some primitive ants receive rather poor infant care. The workers merely throw the meat of insects down beside them, and they have to find their food by squirming around in their nursery chambers.

The larvae of many ants develop into naked pupae. As their bodies develop, the appendages, segments, and eyes can be seen through the transparent skin. Later, the developing pupae move their legs, antennae, and mouth parts and their bodies become darker. Meanwhile, the nursemaids lick their skins intently and assist the pupae as they emerge from their larval skins.

The larvae of other ants spin cocoons and develop within these silken covers into young ants. These cocoons, which are tan or white and for some ants are one-fourth inch or more in length, are often mistaken for ant eggs. Ant eggs of most species are smaller than the head of a pin and

Worker ants guard, clean, and move cocoons to areas of favorable temperature.

for tiny ants are almost invisible to the naked eye.

Ant larvae usually cannot spin cocoons unless they are first buried in the soil or debris of the nest. Then they must be unearthed and cleaned off by the nursemaid workers, which move them about in the nest to places of favorable moisture and temperature.

Many times I have watched the workers in my artificial ant nests assist at the birth of an ant from a cocoon. The workers help tear open the end of the silken cover. Then one or more ants hold the cocoon while another pulls out and assists the callow adult. The young ant is pale in color and unsteady on its legs. The workers groom it, and if it is a young male or queen they assiduously lick its wings. The callow can feed itself and eventually becomes a full-fledged member of the colony.

In addition to the production of worker ants, there comes a time in nearly every ant colony when new queens and males are produced. This may occur during the early summer, and these winged ants may fly in the same season. Some species produce queens and males that remain in the nest over winter and then leave in a marriage swarm in the following spring.

The mating flight of winged ants has long been believed to occur only under favorable conditions of temperature, moisture, and other meteorological conditions. But recent studies by E. S. McCluskey of harvester ants and Argentine ants have demonstrated the existence of internal rhythms in male ants that may trigger the flights, rather than weather conditions alone.

Internal factors also cause the males of many ant species to fly from the nest at different times than the females from the same nest. This ensures cross breeding, since females from one colony will have flights that coincide with male flights from neighboring nests.

Much preparation for the marriage flight goes on in an ant nest. The requirements differ with the species. The females of fungus-growing ants, for example, each carry a pellet of fungus in their mouth cavities so the garden can be started in the new nest.

M. J. Way (1963) reports that the virgin females of a tropical ant, *Acropyga paramaribensis,* carry fertilized female coccids in their mandibles. Thus the new ant colony will be assured of a supply of honeydew produced by the root-feeding coccids.

Many people have seen flying ant swarms and have believed they were gnat swarms. Réaumur, who wrote *The Natural History of Ants,*

Young ant, or callow, ready to emerge from cocoon.

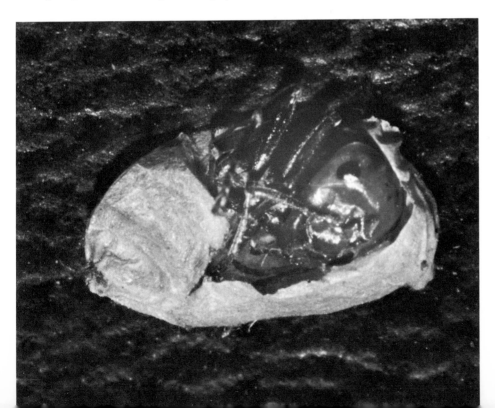

Carpenter ant queens before the nuptial flight. Some cocoons have not hatched.

tells how he saw a small cloud of insects near Tours, France, in 1731, and captured some in his hand. They were winged and in pairs. Then he knew they were mating ants.

Some recent visitors to our home in Portland, Oregon, saw what they believed to be a swarm of very large mosquitoes in our back yard. Actually they were small carpenter ants that had emerged from a cherry tree stump where I had been observing them for two years.

Ant marriage flights can be observed almost anywhere, from large cities to mountaintops. John K. Terres observed the little honey ants *Prenolepis imparis* swarming out of holes in the ground on April 18 in Central Park, New York City. On the Great Plains in Colorado and Wyoming I used to watch for the flights of countless millions of harvester ants about August 10 each year. Numerous reports of flying ants on the summits of western mountains have been published.

The marriage flight of ants lasts but a short time. When copulation has been accomplished in the air, the ants come to earth. The male soon dies. The female breaks off her wings and begins the search for a favorable place to start her new home. The newly fertilized female may contain as many as three hundred million sperm, enough to fertilize all the eggs that ever will be produced during the existence of her colony.

Her first task is to excavate a burrow or closed chamber, in which she remains for many weeks or months. Nourishment comes from her wing muscles, which dissolve in the blood plasma. Finally she lays a few eggs and carefully nurtures them and the young larvae and pupae, which become the first workers. These workers, though small and few in number, bring in food for the queen and for the larger workers which soon appear. Then the establishment and intricate development of the colony begins. If it is undisturbed it may flourish for many years.

The enemies of ants, however, are legion. Some of these are specialized for preying on ants and termites. The spiny anteater, Australian banded anteater, tropical American anteater, Old World pangolin, and aardvark all have claws that enable them to tear open ant nests. Some of these animals explore ant galleries with long protractile sticky tongues. The six-foot-long aardvark of Africa feeds mainly on termites, but it also consumes ant eggs, cocoons, and adults.

Harvester ants in August, when the winged reproductives are starting to emerge.

Wild animals in the temperate regions of North America do not depend primarily on ants as food. Bears, however, frequently tear decaying logs apart and will eat carpenter ant larvae, cocoons, and adults when they are present. Skunks, mice, and shrews occasionally find and eat ants, but these are minor parts of their diets.

Carpenter ant queen. Note the characteristic sharp spine on the petiole (center), and the large thorax containing the wing muscles.

The greatest enemies of wood-inhabiting ants are the woodpeckers. In winter, the diet of the pileated woodpecker consists largely of carpenter ants, which live in colonies in standing trees as well as in logs on the ground. Carpenter ant queens also hibernate beneath the bark of dead trees. In the Blue Mountains of Oregon, I have seen pileated woodpeckers, which are as large as crows, dig holes four inches deep in dead ponderosa pine trees within a few minutes to obtain the ants hidden in their tunnels.

Winged ant males and queens, during the nuptial flight, are especially vulnerable to capture by birds and others animals. John C. Moser states that mated queens of town ants in Louisiana, after they drop to the ground, are captured by armadillos, birds, and ground beetles.

Town ants, *Atta texana,* and a small ant, *Iridomyrmex pruinosus,* related to the Argentine ant have been found in the stomachs of common nighthawks in Louisiana. Apparently the nighthawks collected the winged ants during a swarming period before and after daylight. The imported Argentine ant *Iridomyrmex humilus* does not have a mating flight. Instead, the females drop their wings and remain within the nest until they become egg producing. Thus they are not vulnerable to night-flying birds.

A great many common birds eat ants* as they are found along with caterpillars, scale insects, beetles, bugs, spiders, weevils, and other insects. Among ant-eating birds are the blue jay, rose-breasted grosbeak, slate-colored junco, Carolina chickadee, brown creeper, dickcissel, and yellow-shafted flicker. The purple finch and the American goldfinch eat aphids, which furnish food for ants.

Among the ant's natural enemies are other insects. The larvae of certain dermestids that infest the hair and skin of dead animals are voracious and seize ants by the tips of their abdomens and cling until the ants are exhausted. Assassin bugs have legs equipped with adhesive pads that enable them to grasp and hold ants while they insert their beaks.

---

* *Editor's Note:* In 1932, W. L. McAtee, a bird food habits investigator of the U. S. Biological Survey, reported more than twelve thousand records of ant eating by more than three hundred species of North American birds up to that time. He concluded that virtually all species of North American birds eat ants at some time and that it would be difficult to name another group of insects so thoroughly preyed upon. Among birds, stomach analyses of their food habits showed that they generally ate 200 to 300 at a meal: swallows often took 800 or more; the nighthawks, 1,000; and woodpeckers, 2,000 or more. One yellow-shafted flicker had eaten 3,000 ants; another, 5,000. Harvester ants were eaten by twenty-five species of birds, of which two Texan nighthawks had eaten 200 and 400 respectively.

The armadillo, common in Texas, digs for ants with its snout. (Tex
Parks & Wildlife Department)

Bears tear logs apart to obtain
ants, cocoons, and larvae.

Flickers are especially fond of ants. (Oregon Gam
Commission.)

In the early evening, the nighthawk awakes from its
summer's-day sleep to prey on flying ants.

Two formidable enemies: the lizard and the toad.

Flying ants are favorite morsels for yellow jackets, here eating fresh salmon meat.

A specialized East Indian bug, *Ptilocerus ochraceus,* exudes a substance from a gland beneath the red hairs on its abdomen that attracts ants. When the ant licks this substance it becomes paralyzed and then is sucked dry by the bug.

Predation by Vespula wasps is common. Many years ago, when I was doing research on the Wasatch Plateau above Ephraim, Utah, the yellow jackets in July daily dropped hundreds of fly and ant heads on my bed in a tent in an aspen grove. Last year in my back yard in Portland, Oregon, yellow jackets, *Vespula diabolica fernaldi,* caught winged carpenter ants as the flight emerged from wood I kept on our patio.

J. A. Chapman has reported similar predation by *Vespula pennsylvanica* at Lake Cowichan, British Columbia. The wasps used their forelegs and middle legs to hold winged *Formica subnuda* ants. These wasps hung by their hind legs, head downward, while they bit off the heads and chewed ant fragments.

Probably the most fascinating, and patient, ant enemies are the "doodlebugs," or ant lions. These are the pit-digging, ugly (if not repulsive) larvae of delicate, long-winged adult insects, with globular eyes and slender abdomens, which resemble damsel flies. These have been nicely described by Jerome and Barbara Rozen. William Morton Wheeler called them "demons of the dust" and wrote a large book about all the species of the world.

Ant lions are common in Europe and in many places in the United States. Last summer, when I visited a large *Formica* ant mound south

90

Ant lion larva. Ants, spiders, and other insects, once caught in the hollow jaws, are sucked dry.

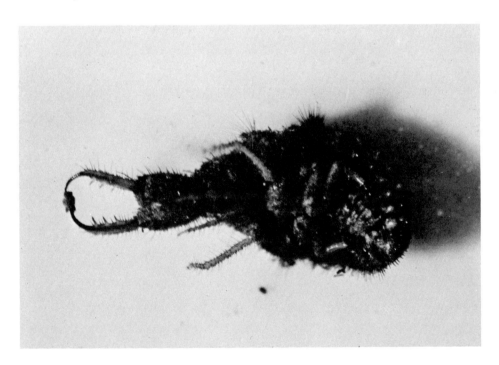

Underside of the ant lion larva. A particle of sand is clamped between the jaws and the larva is "playing possum."

Pit of an ant lion larva. It can move only backward through the dust or sand. Arrow points to carpenter ant hole in log.

of Mount Hood in Oregon, the ant lions were busily throwing up "smoke puffs" from their funnels in the dust.

I watched one ant lion pit and could see the course of its owner as it traveled up the side of its dust funnel, out beyond to a distance of an inch, and then back to its funnel. All this I observed by seeing the soil being heaved as by a miniature mole. Finally the creature settled itself with only its jaws protruding at the bottom of its pit. It easily captured an ant I threw into the pit.

At home, I kept ant lions in jelly glasses filled with granulated sugar. The larvae make perfect pits and throw sugar to a distance of 12 to 16 inches by scooping it on their heads and jaws and snapping their heads upward. They construct their pits by moving backward in a spiral as the pit deepens. They have no forward gear and are capable only of backing into their powdery substratum.

I have become so attached to my pet ants that I do not feed them to the ant lions; I use spiders instead. On August 7, 1966, I fed a white spider with a leg spread of three fourths of an inch to an ant lion that was only five sixteenths of an inch long. The battle lasted some thirty seconds and then the spider was pulled under the sugar. This ant lion did not accept another spider until March 23, 1967.

The record reported in the literature belongs to an ant lion that went without food for 240 days. In nature, an ant surely would fall into the pit before that much time had passed.

Trout and other fish are enemies of ants. Many species of ants live in meadows, along stream sides, and on vegetation that grows in ponds and lakes. Ants are not injured by falling into water, but they are likely to serve as fish food before they regain the safety of vegetation or dry land.

Edward Ringwood Hewitt, in his book *Telling on the Trout,* concluded that the tartness of ants was as attractive to fish as sour pickles are to us. Certainly trout take ants in large numbers when they are available.

Trout flies are tied to imitate many species of ants. Among favorite patterns are the black ant, honey ant, red ant, cinnamon ant, red and brown ant, carpenter ant, and minute black ant.

Among the ant's other natural enemies are mold, floods, drought, high temperatures, and lizards. Some species of toads subsist almost entirely on ants. Narrow-mouth toads, spadefoot toads, and Woodhouse toads are especially fond of ants and obtain them by sitting near the entrances to the ant nests.

Carnivorous plants that grow in bogs and wet situations are collectors

A doodlebug can be cleaned in a sieve. If put in a deep dish containing sand or dust, it will dig a new pit and feed on ants or spiders placed in the dish.

of ants. The Venus's flytrap, for example, produces a secretion that attracts insects to its leaves. When an insect touches the bristles the leaf snaps shut and the victim is digested by enzymes produced by the plant.

More than 450 species of plant carnivores are found around the world. Among those commonly seen in this country are the sundews of the genus *Drosera,* the trumpet plant, *Sarracenia flava,* the pitcher plant, *S. purpurea,* and the magnificent "cobra orchid," *Darlingtonia californica,* which is found in bogs near the Oregon and California coasts.

The pitcher plants and cobra plants are equipped with hairs that point downward so that insects entering the trap can proceed only downward into the liquid pool inside the leaf. In *Sarracenia* the liquid contains digestive enzymes, whereas, in *Darlingtonia,* bacteria in the liquid disintegrate the victim.

Ants frequently are trapped in the slits between the nectar horns of milkweed flowers. This device also traps bumblebees, which pull away the pollen-bearing paddles and escape. But ants, not being strong enough to pull free, remain anchored and eventually starve or die in the sun's heat.

Little is known about diseases, bacteria, viruses, and pathogenic organisms that affect ants. Unlike flies and cockroaches, ants are among the cleanest of creatures and consequently avoid many of the infestations common to other insects.

Molds, however, are known to kill ant queens in their nests. Also, one of the tiny ergot fungi grows on ant bodies, but the infestation may occur after the ant has died from other causes.

The worst enemy of ants, as of most other wild creatures, is man. Man's blows are dealt in multitudinous ways: by destruction of forests and grasslands, by building and road construction, by importation of destructive insects, and by such a plethora of fertilizers, poisons, and soil and air pollutants that it is a wonder that any ant survives in the natural habitat.

One of the strange partnerships in nature, in which ants are not neces-

Darlingtonia plants capture ants and other insects that crawl into the opening under the "cobra hood."

sarily prey, is that in which flocks of birds follow columns of army ants on the march. A glimpse of one of these flocks, which may consist of black-and-white jungle "ant birds" and camp followers such as puff-birds, motmots, wrens, flycatchers, and tanagers, is evidence of a major column of ants that may be moving over a front from 3 to 20 yards wide.

The ants are not particularly molested by the birds, which chase the spiders and insects flushed by the ants from the litter on the forest floor. Edwin O. Willis, who has made extensive studies of the army ants, *Eciton burchelli* and *Labidus praedator* on Barro Colorado Island, Panama Canal Zone, states that some birds, such as ocellated ant thrushes, are professional or regular ant followers.

The professionals forage on the ground among the ants. "Amateurs," such as the plain-brown woodcreeper, forage in the higher and less productive peripheral zones along the army's line of march when the regular ant-following birds are present.

This air force of scavenger birds frequently is accompanied by flies, which lay eggs on large victims of the ants; these may include tarantulas, scorpions, lizards, young birds, snakes, and even monkeys.

Ant birds sometimes herald the progress of the raiding army by singing and shrieking. The people in native villages thus are warned of the approaching army.

An ornithological—or myrmecological—mystery is why many birds use ants as part of their toilets. Bird "anting" is a preening action in which ants are rubbed on the primary wing feathers and sometimes on the tail feathers. During the action the bird goes through many contortions, loses its balance, and seems to experience an ecstasy that makes it oblivious to its companions or its surroundings.

According to John K. Terres, over 160 kinds of birds are known to practice anting. Twenty-four species of ants have been used by anting birds.

From the first observation published in 1831 by John James Audubon of wild turkeys rolling in ants' nests, many references and statements

Ants are common in vegetation growing above the high-tide mark of the Pacific Ocean near Tillamook, Oregon.

have been published on the anting habit. Frank W. Lane has quoted some of these in his book, *Animal Wonder World*. In essence, the statements, even of experienced ornithologists, show much diversity of description of the performance and of opinion as to its meaning.

Hance Roy Ivor in Canada probably has witnessed more birds anting under controlled conditions than any other man. In his aviary he has watched nearly thirty species of birds ant and has seen the performance thousands of times.

Baltimore orioles, robins, cardinals, blue jays, starlings, and catbirds have readily anted in Ivor's observatory. His pet crow, however, did not ant like other birds but seemed to derive pleasure when ants crawled over its plumage.

Various theories have been evolved to explain the true purpose of anting. Holger Poulsen, a Danish ornithologist, concluded that the action was to remove formic acid squirted on the birds' plumage by ants.

97

Ivor does not agree, since his camera studies show no evidence that his birds rub their heads against their feathers while anting.

Other theories include the suggestion that birds place ants in their feathers as a source of food on migration. But birds ant when they are not migrating. Other observers believe ants are used to rid the bird of parasites, either by having the ants carry the parasites away or because the formic acid repels the parasites. It has been suggested that birds ant for pure enjoyment. In any event, Ivor believes that anting is a primal form of behavior that some birds have retained and some have lost, and that a definitive solution to the puzzle has not been found.

In all this controversy, it seems to me that the ant has been neglected. No definitive study has been made of the chemical substances produced by ants that might produce reactions in a bird similar to the ecstasy of a cat over catnip. But chemical substances that are structurally related to nepetalactone, the physiologically active principle of catnip, have been isolated from ants.

Cavill and Robertson have recently given us an insight into the enormously complex and poorly understood secretions used by ants as chemical messengers in their social organization. Ants use secretions called "pheromones" for communication. They use venoms in attack and defense. And they use alluring sweet-scented or sweet-tasting fluids to attract individuals to their communities. A substance isolated from the anal glands of the Argentine ant even possesses insecticidal activity. So maybe some of the birds do use ants to rid themselves of parasites.

At least, with the recent development of modern techniques in chromatography and spectroscopy, it is now becoming possible to analyze and evaluate the functions of some of the infinitesimal glandular secretions of ants. Maybe if the chemists, the ornithologists, and the myrmecologists were to pool their efforts they might find an acceptable explanation of bird anting.

Autumn

AUTUMN IS A TIME OF URGENCY for the ants. The unfailing warmth of summer and its profusion of food now is replaced by wider fluctuations of weather and by different foods produced by the ripening harvest. Ants that have their greatest activities in autumn must make efficient use of the ever-shortening periods when the microclimates of their little worlds are favorable.

The weather near the ground, in logs, or on plant stems is more important to the ants than the weather we humans experience in our broader world above. To an ant the sunlit or the shaded side of a stone can make the difference between September and November in a minute of walking time.

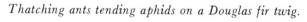

Thatching ants tending aphids on a Douglas fir twig.

In early autumn the aphid-tending ants are especially active. Their cows have produced a population explosion and are sucking the last juices from goldenrods, asters, and a thousand other plants that are still green and flourishing. When the foliage dries the aphids no longer will be able to supply honeydew and must be carried to the ant nests for the winter hibernation.

For harvester ants the seed supply is at a maximum. There still are seeds of cryptantha, plantain, globe mallow, and short-lived annuals that grew in spring and summer. These must be gleaned from the ground. In addition, there are seeds of grasses and autumn herbs to be found and carried to the granaries in the nest.

Internal changes in nest construction and colony activity must be made. In June, the temperature maximum occurred on the southeast slope of the harvester ant mound. That was where the ants built their doorway. By autumn, the temperature is greatest on the southwest slope. And that is where the doorway frequently occurs.

The twig and leaf mounds of the thatching ants become more dome-like in autumn, since efficiency in heat absorption and retention is necessary for the winter comfort of the colony. A hemispherical dome at noon on December 21, at latitude 47 degrees, receives twice as much insolation or solar energy as does the level ground surface owing to the angle at which the sun's rays are received. Furthermore, the thatching ants usually place their nests so that evergreen trees will not shade them from the winter sun.

One may sometimes wonder why the little dooryard and meadow ants still continue their travels when the cool autumn days require humans to wear coats for comfort. Unless the air is turbulent, the ants actually are wandering in a thin layer of air above the ground surface that is much warmer than the air around us.

I am convinced that carpenter ants make daily and seasonal adjustments to the microclimatic zones in fallen tree trunks where they live. The segment near the top of a log, on the southwest side, may have a

Author and thatching ant mound in Mount Hood National Forest, Oregon.

temperature 15 or 20 degrees higher than the air temperature. The underside and the constantly shaded portions of the log may be too cold for insect larvae to complete their development.

Great activity occurs in large ant nests in autumn, since different internal temperatures are available for colony adjustment. This has been shown by measurements made in the great nests of the forest ant, *Formica rufa,* in Germany. Even in cloudy and rainy weather the nest temperature about 10 inches below the surface was about 5 to 7 degrees F. warmer than the surrounding air. The sunny side of the nest was 9 to 16 degrees F. warmer than the shady side. The design of the nest was such that the ants could move from one microclimate to another to obtain the most favorable temperatures for their colony activities.

Scherba reported that relative humidity in nest chambers of *Formica ulkei* is much less variable in comparison with that of the surrounding soil. The workers adjust the mound structure in response to changes in soil drainage and shading.

In early autumn, great activity in many ant nests centers around the production of more males and queens. By late August the little nests of

Formica ants, having moved into the galleries carved by carpenter ants, are carrying juniper twigs into their nest.

the orchard-dwelling ant *Prenolepis imparis* contain many young males and females. These overwinter in the ground and mate in the following spring.

Many species of carpenter ants also produce sexual forms that can be found in tree stumps and soft wood from autumn until the following spring. The ant exterminator man who lives near our home in Portland has given me many of these winged ants for study. He calls them "swarmers."

Numerous ants make their nuptial flights in early autumn. Edward O. Wilson has reported flights of the common ant *Lasius neoniger* during September on Long Island, New York, and in the Boston area. In Denver, Colorado, flights have been observed as late as October 13. The fecundated queens overwinter without broods and start laying eggs in the following spring.

Nuptial swarms of *Lasius niger* and *Myrmica rubra* in early autumn sometimes contain so many ants they are visible from afar like clouds of smoke. The fertilized queens make shallow burrows, which are closed to the outside world. There they remain until spring.

Autumn

Contrary to the belief of some people, the final food harvest by ants in autumn is not to provide food for the colony during the winter. In our cold northern climate, the ants that hibernate need little or no food in winter. The harvester ant colonies and the nests of wood ants and carpenter ants I have excavated in winter have not had food stored.

Food storage frequently has its greatest survival value in summer. During the severe drought of 1939 in northeastern Colorado, I observed how harvester ants survived a summer of virtually no rain by living on seeds stored in late spring. The superabundant spring crop of peppergrass, plains plantain, cryptantha, six-weeks fescue, lamb's-quarters, and other ephemeral plants was avidly harvested by *Pogonomyrmex occidentalis* from late April until July. From then until early winter, virtually no rain fell on the parched prairies and no grass seeds were produced. But the ant granaries still contained seeds in September and the ant colonies were in flourishing condition in the spring of 1940 when the rains came.

It seems reasonable to suppose that harvester ants store seeds against periods when food may be unavailable. These may be periods of drought or of protracted wet weather when vegetative growth is at a maximum but no seeds are produced. The ants instinctively guard against nonproductive periods by collecting food when it is present in superabundant quantities. But they do not collect it for use in cold winters.

Excavations of the harvester ant *Pogonomyrmex owyheei* by Willard

Carpenter ant queens emerging from nest at edge of a tree stump.

Honey ants hanging from the ceiling of their chamber in the Garden of the Gods, Colorado. (Paul W. Nesbit)

and Crowell near Redmond, Oregon, in the winter of 1963, revealed masses of almost completely dormant ants at depths varying from 6 to 96 inches. Occasionally, the ants made slight movements of antennae or legs. Few or no seed stores were found, and the observers concluded that these ants do not store seeds for a winter food supply.

The honey ants and other ants that have repletes—workers with abdomens modified for storage of honeydew and other liquids—forage for sweets in fall and fill their "honey jars." This stored food is used in the following spring by the developing brood and by the males and females, which fly during the first warm days of April.

As Creighton has pointed out, honey ant repletes can be formed only by callow ants, which can expand their abdominal tissues while they are still very young. If callows are produced at a time when honey is not available, there may be no repletes to store food for times of summer scarcity or overwinter for use in the following spring.

Lack of stored food does not mean the death of the colony. Most species of ants, even including the highly specialized fungus-growing ants, are sufficiently omnivorous to pass to other kinds of food, including even their own larvae and pupae, if necessary. Ants in warm climates and in the tropics, of course, have little need to store food since their supplies of insects, seeds, honeydew, or fungi are almost constantly available.

Ants that do considerable work above ground do much traveling in obtaining food, collecting nest materials, and making raids on other species. Autumn is a good time to study their trail-making methods and the factors that affect their movements. Their running speed, for example, varies with the size of ant, the length of legs, temperature, and the kind of work being done.

Very small ants, such as *Aphaenogaster subterranea,* wander slowly over the ground on warm evenings at the rate of 1 to 2 inches per minute. Wood ants, following their trails from nest to aphid-bearing trees in eastern Oregon, covered 3 to 6 inches per minute on beaten trails when the air temperature was 65 degrees F. In the southern Utah desert, when the surface temperature of unshaded ground on September 27, 1966, was approximately 96 degrees F., I timed harvester ants running across their cleared circles at an average rate of 13.2 feet per minute.

Many ants make scent trails by releasing a chemical, called a pheromone, from Dufour's gland in their abdomens. The chemical is volatile and the trail laid by a single ant may last only a few minutes. Trailways

Harvester ants running over their cleared area in the heat of the sun.

that are traveled by hundreds of workers, however, receive sufficient chemical to last for several days.

Trails left by ants returning from a food discovery may be directional so their fellow workers know which way to go. Ants are not confused by the trails of other species, since each kind of ant appears to have its own odor substance.

Law, Wilson, and McCloskey have reported that the minor workers of *Pheidole fallax,* which lives in the West Indies, lay odor trails, whereas the soldiers do not. Apparently, the Dufour's gland in the soldiers is greatly reduced or absent. The soldiers, however, readily follow the worker trails.

John C. Moser reported an interesting experiment with the trail-marking substances of the town ant. Chemicals from the poison sacs of the ants were applied to paper in a circle about six inches in diameter. Worker ants readily followed the artificial trail. But of greater interest was the observation that female adults of a wingless roach, *Attaphila fungicola,* which inhabits the fungus gardens of the ants, also followed the trail while keeping their maxillary palps in constant contact with the paper.

The common ant *Prenolepis imparis* was observed by Mary Talbot to have two types of foraging activity. Single individuals wandered at random and carried small food particles to the nest. But when large pieces of food, such as decaying fruit or earthworms, were discovered, a distinct odor trail was laid and numerous workers followed it slavishly between nest and food. Colored toothpicks were used to mark these trails and the ants paralleled them as though they were guide posts.

When trailways are not readily apparent, the travels of ants can be detected by marking the ants with paint or with radioactive phosphorus. Hamp W. Echols, in a study of leaf-cutting ants in Louisiana, marked eight hundred workers with paint. Four hours later, twenty-three of the marked ants were found excavating subsoil from a mound 68 feet from the hole they had entered. Other marked ants were found foraging twenty-four hours later approximately 100 yards from the original starting point.

Paul B. Kannowski, using radioactive tracers, found that *Lasius minutus* ants, bog inhabiters that rarely appear on the surface, traveled through tunnels from their nests to roots and underground stems of grasses where they were cultivating aphids. Honey, tagged with radioactive phosphorus, was carried by the workers to the larvae, which then became radioactive.

Food sharing and exchange is the basis for existence among ants. It has always seemed to me that ants are the ultimate examples of loving one's neighbors. An ant returning from a long journey will on demand give of its honeydew to another ant just leaving the nest. The traveler then will turn back and repeat the long journey for more food. The recipient, of course, may soon share food from its crop with other ants in the nest.

I give water to the ants in my observation colonies by trickling a spoonful down the glass sides of their cage. Almost immediately a few ants lap up the droplets until their gasters swell and the plates on their abdomens are pulled apart. Within an hour every ant in the colony has a swollen gaster because the water bearers have shared with all their associates.

Food and water exchange is initiated by the soliciting ant palpitating or caressing the donor ant with forelegs or antennae. Usually the palpitation is on the head of the donor. The internal valve from the crop is

Ants following an odor trail to food.

opened and the donor regurgitates a drop of liquid, which is accepted by the soliciting ant. Sometimes the donor ant offers the liquid, particularly to larvae, without being solicited.

Food exchange in large colonies involves a chain of transfers. Ants in the field may pass food to carriers that go to the nest. There further transfer occurs between workers. Frequently the larvae and queens are among the last to receive food.

Food exchange has been studied by placing dye in soybean oil or other bait. Microscopic examination soon reveals the presence of dye in the digestive tracts of nonforaging workers, indicating exchange in the nest. The dye also can be seen in the postpharyngeal glands, which are associated with the digestive system. When viewed from the front, the

Ants exchanging food by regurgitation.

Ants eat dead crickets. Some crickets that live in ant nests are so tiny they can crawl up an ant's leg.

lower part of the ant's face is darkened by the dye in the glands inside its head.

In ant colonies with repletes, food storage and exchange are developed to a high degree. At moderate temperatures, and in periods of food abundance, foraging workers collect honeydew and pass it to the repletes for storage. A supply is thus built up for use when hot dry weather make outside supplies unavailable. Then the flow is reversed as the workers receive food from their living storage bins.

There are reports in the ant literature that two different species may live in the same nest and mutually exchange food. In a sense, this could be called double parasitism. Few ant species, however, live together amicably.

The small ants of the genus *Leptothorax* have a tendency to build their nests adjoining the nest of some larger species of ant. It is not uncommon to see tiny craters only an inch or two in diameter on the sides of the mounds of harvester ants. Apparently the two kinds of ants live in peaceful coexistence.

A still higher order of association has been described by Creighton. *Leptothorax provancheri* builds its nests so the tunnels open into the larger passage ways of *Myrmica brevinodis,* where the two species mingle. The *Leptothorax* ants climb on their hosts and lick the surfaces of

109

their bodies, probably to secure an edible secretion. Creighton states, "Myrmica workers will solicit a back-scratching by regurgitating food to the Leptothorax workers. What the Myrmica workers gain, aside from a thorough cleaning, is not clear."

Ants, of course, are notable for keeping other insect guests and parasites in their nests. Some of these guests are commensals, some are parasites, some are plain "free loaders" or tramps, and some seek only the protection of the nest during winter.

Dr. William W. Mann (1948) observed a motley collection of guests and parasites marching in file in the columns of foraging army ants. Some of these were tubby histerid beetles that looked ludicrous in comparison with the ants. Other beetles in the column resembled the ants in form and coloration. Long-legged wasps without wings, and presumably parasitic on the young ants, also marched in the army.

Dr. Mann noticed that when one of the parasites stopped running it was picked up by an army ant and carried beneath the ant's abdomen along the line of march. He states that no one knows why ants tolerate many of these guests, which do nothing but share in the spoils of the chase.

Certain rove beetles that live in ant colonies eat the ant larvae and pupae. If the adult ants attack, the beetle repels them by ejecting an offensive fluid.

Tiny crickets are common in ant nests. These creatures are so small they can scramble around over legs and body of the ant, meanwhile licking the ants for secretions. The crickets dine on food left in the ant nest and also rear their young among the ants.

A great number of other myrmecophiles, or ant-loving insects, dwell among ants. Some, like the tiny springtails, are almost ignored by the ants. Others secrete substances that the ants like, sometimes to their detriment, since the ants may neglect their own proper food and become victims of malnutrition.

The clavigerid beetle, *Claviger testaceus,* is one of the best known of the ant guests. These blind insects solicit food by stroking the ants with

their antennae. The ants regurgitate food and in turn lick a sweet substance that is secreted by glands on the backs of the beetles.

Other kinds of beetles are useful in ant nests, in that they eat dead
ants and other material that the ants would normally carry to the rub-
bish pile. Still other beetles produce larvae that feed on ant larvae and
thus are parasitic on their hosts.

Altogether it has been estimated that 5,000 myrmecophiles or dwellers
in ant nests have been identified. The motley group includes bugs,
beetles, flies, roaches, mites, spiders, midges, and worms. Because of
nature's system of checks and balances, however, these guests, aliens,
and enemies never kill all the ants or eat them out of house and home.

In northern climates, in autumn, a greater urgency than the need of
food is the necessity to prepare the colony quarters for winter. This is
accomplished by moving to more suitable quarters, repairing the nest,
and digging tunnels and chambers below the frost line and by changes
in the nest population.

In our northern states the soil may freeze to a depth of 5 or 6 feet
unless it is covered by snow. The harvester ants of the plains and prairies
excavate their nests to depths of 8 to 12 feet and thus escape freezing.
Ants in forests and in mountains where snow remains through the winter
do not go to great depths, since heat from the earth beneath the snow
prevents deep freezing.

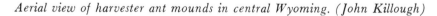

Aerial view of harvester ant mounds in central Wyoming. (John Killough)

Skunks dig ant queens out of shallow nests made soon after the mating flight. (Oregon Game Commission)

Actually, not much is known about the depth of most ant nests in winter. But many of our smallest ants undoubtedly are unable to dig tunnels deep enough to escape the frost of northern winters. Experimental studies have indicated that many species of ants are not injured by freezing. On numerous occasions, I have split firewood containing carpenter ants that had been exposed to temperatures far below zero. When warmed in the house, these ants immediately became active.

In late summer and early autumn, many ant queens, after the mating flight, seek cavities under bark or dig shallow holes in the soil. There they remain for many months, exposed to the low temperatures of winter, awaiting the coming of spring when their eggs can be laid and the new colony can be started.

In established colonies many population changes occur in autumn. The nests of some species have many hundreds of winged, or alate, queens and winged males that remain over winter. The last pale, callow, soft-bodied workers change to deeper-colored, hard-bodied mature ants. Generally, all pupae and cocoons disappear as the young ants change into adults. If accidents or enemies decimate the worker crews in their last food-collecting efforts, the colony goes into winter with reduced numbers, since death losses are not compensated by birth of new ants.

During autumn in our southern states the activities in ant colonies are diminished but do not cease. With the advent of cool weather the ants spend more time in their chambers and less above ground. In tropical regions there is no autumn or winter, and so the cycle of ant habits continues and is interrupted only by droughts, floods, or internal rhythms.

Winter

Ants in our northern latitudes hibernate in winter. They do not necessarily seek shelter from cold, since many species can endure temperatures below freezing. This is particularly true of ants that spend the winter in tree trunks, logs, stumps, and plant stems that are exposed to the elements.

Escape from excessive moisture appears to be more important than escape from cold. Even the shallow nests of little ants contain chambers that slant upward from the central shaft or vertical tunnel. Water poured into this shaft does not enter against air pressure in rooms where the ants are found in winter.

The ground is the great winter resort for the majority of our northern ants. As a rule, ants do not all hibernate at once in the ground. A. M. Holmquist found that the retirement into hibernation of *Formica ulkei* took about six weeks. Many of these ants assembled in clusters about four feet beneath the soil surface. Single ants, found in the frozen mound, probably were stragglers that worked late into the fall months.

Different degrees of dormancy exist among ants. Many of the ground-dwelling ants I have excavated came alive quickly when exposed to heat. Those taken from below the frost line frequently moved their antennae and legs, and some staggered about immediately after excavation. Carpenter ant queens that hibernated under bark and were subject to the extremes of winter cold seemed to be in deeper dormancy than soil-dwelling ants.

Mary Talbot reported that *Prenolepis imparis* does not strictly hiber-

114

Winter world of the thatching ant: snow-covered mound in the Blue Mountains, eastern Oregon.

nate but forages all during the winter when surface temperature of the soil rises above freezing. I believe careful investigation would show that many other ants move about when winter temperatures are favorable. I have seen harvester ants outside their mounds in eastern Colorado as late as December 5 and as early as February 10. In Oregon, in the Cascade Mountains, I have seen carpenter ants outside their nests on warm days in every month of the year.

Ants seen moving in winter are simply taking advantage of momentarily favorable microclimates. When conditions of exposure, color of the ground, air circulation, and heat reception from the sun are optimum, surprisingly high temperatures are attained in logs, in large thatched ant nests, and in the surface ground layer.

Ants that hibernate in snowbound country are less exposed to the rigors of weather than mammals and birds that remain active throughout the year. Snow absorbs more infrared radiation than sand or earth. Snow also insulates the ground. Deep within snow its temperature is only slightly below freezing, even when the air temperature is many degrees below zero. Thus ants in the soil are able to hibernate in relatively moderate temperatures and in an environment where moisture and relative humidity are fairly constant.

Ants in mountainous country frequently build their nests beneath granite boulders. These are good engineering choices for the winter nests, since heat penetrates deeply into granite or rock and radiates less rapidly than from soil.

Some ant nests used in winter represent astounding feats of labor. The acre-sized underground nests of the town ant are made by thousands of ants working for several years. Desert-dwelling ants, which generally are not tolerant of heat or cold, dig deep formicaries. Lloyd Tevis dug 11 feet and did not reach the main granaries of the harvester ant *Veromessor pergandei*. In Arizona, Creighton and Crandall found the queen and repletes of *Myrmecocystus melliger* at 16 feet, after removing fifteen tons of soil, part of which was caliche!

This mound was built against a stump for support.

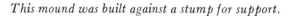

Pillars of earth are sometimes created to support ceilings in underground nests.

Sometimes, with a knowledge of soil structure, it is possible to judge the depth of ant nests by examining the "mine tailings" brought to the surface. Ants that live in the aeolian pumice deposits from Mount Mazama in central Oregon leave craters of fine, granular, dark-brown soil if they are living in the A₁ horizon of the Lapine soil series. Ants that go deeper into the AC horizon bring up loamy coarse sand that may be dark yellow brown. If they go still deeper, the moist gravelly material on their mounds may be yellow. If they go to the buried D horizon beneath the pumice mantle, their excavated material may be dark brown.

The internal structure of ant nests, of course, varies with the needs of the ants and the available materials. Many ground-dwelling ants construct antechambers immediately inside the entrance. Storage and brood chambers usually are dome shaped and thus employ the principle of the arch for support. Pillars of earth sometimes are left to support the ceilings of large chambers. Floors, walls, and ceilings of nest chambers usually are very smooth and even. Galleries leading to chambers frequently are sloped upward so as to minimize flooding by water.

The internal placement of galleries and vertical shafts in earthen mounds and in the domed twig nests of thatching ants is arranged to permit easy movement from one side of the nest to another. Provision also is made for vertical transfer of the brood to favorable temperature zones.

The manner in which ants do their engineering work can best be observed in artificial nests with glass sides. Here are some of my notes on *Formica* ants working in my study on November 1, 1966:

Every ant, 100 or more, seems to be occupied. Twigs and fir needles are being carried, projecting ahead of the ant. They remind me of Irishmen ready to toss the caber. Others are carrying logs like straddle buggies in a lumber mill, each log projecting in front and behind the ant. Some of the large logs, six times the length of the ant and twice its diameter, are being pulled from one end with the ant going backward, all legs working and sometimes skidding on the glass side of the cage.

Now two ants are dragging one stick, working in tandem, one ant pulling at the end, the other pulling at the middle. Another ant is holding the end of a log in her mandibles, and pushing instead of pulling. If the stick falls down into the log jam, she goes down and sets her mandibles again. Then she backs up through the labyrinth with her burden. If her effort were put into human dimensions it would be analogous to six-foot men carrying, lifting, and pulling logs one to three feet in diameter.

Imagine yourself going down into a log jam 300 feet deep, extracting a two-foot-thick Douglas fir log 20 to 30 feet in length and dragging it by hand to the surface of the pile in ten minutes, only to have it fall back 100 feet and have to do the job all over again. To top it off, imagine other men running roughshod over your back, head, and legs, pulling other logs that get tangled with your log.

I have long been intrigued by the apparent waste of effort whereby

Ants are always trying to take sticks and other objects into the nest. They generally succeed.

ants carry sticks and stones up the sides of their mounds, over the top, and down the other side before depositing them. Many times they pass one another, going in opposite directions. Close observation, however, leads me to believe that an engineering principle is involved. Frequently the ant actually pushes the stone or twig into place instead of merely dropping it. Thus, with the aid of gravity, the nest materials are wedged together and not merely piled one upon another.

It is a matter of speculation, of course, how the ants are able to perform these individual labors and achieve in the end a nest so structured and designed as to take advantage of insolation, to provide air spaces for temperature control, and to guard against destructive physical forces in nature. Whether it is instinct alone or a form of intelligence, I do not know.

I do know that ant nests are so well constructed for the needs of each species that the ants have relatively few enemies in winter. Freezing does not bother them. Floods seldom occur. Bears, which tear apart logs and stumps, hibernate when the ants hibernate in northern woods. Only the woodpeckers remain as active enemies in winter.

The destruction of ant colonies is most likely to occur in spring, summer, and fall. And in those seasons the ants increase their numbers and thus offset the inroads of enemies.

Ants are relatively long-lived insects. The workers and soldiers may live for three years. The average life of a queen has been estimated at twelve years, and some have lived as long as twenty years. Males ordinarily live only a few weeks and quickly die after the mating. Some species of *Camponotus* and *Prenolepis,* however, have males in the nest from fall until they mate with queens in the following spring.

The longevity of mounds and colonies is not necessarily dependent on the life expectancy of a single queen. Many ant species have numerous queens in their nests, and when old queens die they are replaced by new ones. Ant colonies also move from one nest to another and thereby perpetuate the activity in large ant cities. W. A. Dreyer reported

(1942) that a large group of mound nests of the ant *Formica ulkei* existed in Lemont Township near Palos Park, Illinois, for at least fifty years. Individual mounds were estimated to be twenty to twenty-five years old.

Some of the harvester ant mounds I marked with iron stakes in 1939 in eastern Colorado were still present when I visited them in September, 1966.

The survival of a whole species of ants sometimes is threatened more by invasions of foreign ants than by the activities of man. The Argentine ant *Iridomyrmex*, for example, which originally came from Brazil, for many years has been on a world-wide conquest of other ants. The native ants have begun to disappear wherever it has appeared. This warlike ant is a pest in houses. In the open it attacks chickens and most kinds of insects, including other ants. It is now established in the southern states and in California. It has journeyed overseas in shipments of food to South Africa, Spain, Italy, France, Germany, and to many islands. When the Argentine ants were introduced into Madeira the *Pheidole* ants disappeared. Elsewhere, the battle is still going on.

These wars between invading ants and native ants are different from the slave-making raids of ants that practice various forms of parasitism. Invading ants wage all-out battles to the death. And frequently the invaders are outstandingly equipped with sicklelike jaws, agility, and nomadic habits that enable them to conquer native ants.

Ants, even of the same genus or species, may replace their own kind. Shortly after World War I a dark form of the fire ant *Solenopsis saevissima* arrived in Mobile, Alabama, from Argentina and became established in that region. In the 1930s a reddish form of this ant was introduced. In less than ten years the black forms were decimated by interbreeding and internecine warfare. Now mostly the red population of the introduced fire ants prevails.

Ant battles are gruesome spectacles. In massed battle the seething multitudes are locked in mortal combat. No quarter is given. Heads

Some Formica *ant mounds, like this one near* La Grande, Oregon, *are ten feet in diameter.*

and abdomens are pierced by needle-sharp mandibles. Even the armor of the thorax is crushed. Legs and antennae are clipped. And individual ants cling to other individuals with bulldog tenacity for hours. Some observers have reported struggles between two ants that lasted for sixteen hours.

In contrast to this internecine war, the slave raids for pupae of other species are more like strategic war than massed battles of decimation. The slave raiders nearly always win and carry away their booty. But they do not kill all the inhabitants of the raided nest. When the slavers return to their homes they become peaceful again.

William Morton Wheeler many years ago summarized the nature of social parasitism among ants. Since 1910 when his book, *Ants,* was published, many new parasitic species have been studied and their habits described. But Wheeler's general account still is unsurpassed even by the recent literature. He recognized four degrees of ant parasites: the temporary social parasites, the facultative slave makers, the

121

obligatory slave makers, and the degenerate slave makers and permanent social parasites.

Under temporary social parasitism, the ants live in mixed colonies. The condition usually starts by invasion of a colony by a queen ant of another species. Or she may even be seized and dragged into the host nest. If a *Bothriomyrmex* queen is taken in by *Tapinoma* workers, she may climb on the back of the host queen and saw off her head. As she has acquired the colony odor, the nest workers accept her, feed her, and care for her young. Eventually the host workers die of old age and the nest changes to a pure colony of *Bothriomyrmex* ants.

There are many other forms of temporary social parasitism among ants. The host species, for example, is not always parasitized by other species. And many mixed colonies are found in which the host queen is not eliminated.

The facultative slave makers have the faculty or ability to make slaves of other ants but can live independently of slaves. The most notable example is the sanguinary, or blood-red, slave maker, *Formica sanguinea,* of Europe. These belligerent ants normally enslave members of the *Formica fusca* group of ants. Their plundering expeditions are made in the daytime.

Scouts locate the nest to be pillaged. Then the army moves up, surrounds the nest, and waits until additional forces arrive. The besieged ants try to fight or escape with their young, but the sanguinary ants intercept them, pour into the nest, kill the owners that offer resistance, and then march home with their stolen larvae and cocoons. The pillaged colony then takes up the task of rearing any young that remain, or they await the development of a new brood.

The Amazon ants, or obligatory slave makers, are truly dependent on their slaves. On raids they are among the fiercest of ants. But they are incapable of digging their own nests, caring for their own young, or even feeding themselves. All these labors have to be done by the enslaved workers that hatch from stolen cocoons.

One of the common American Amazons is *Polyergus breviceps.* Their slaves are *Formica* ants, usually *F. argentata, subsericea,* or *neocinerea.* Unlike the sanguine ants, which may raid other colonies only once in a summer, the Amazons make forays almost daily. When they return home, the slaves in their own nest rush out in apparent excitement over the plunder that has been collected.

For some unaccountable reason the victims of these raids seem to make little defense of their broods, and the kidnapers do not harm their victims. After repeated plundering, however, the slave colonies sometimes move to other locations to avoid their enemies.

The permanent social parasites include groups of ants that are dependent throughout life on their hosts. The slave-host ants care for their own broods and those of their conquerors. The queens of the host species are allowed to survive, and thus colonies of thousands of both kinds of ants live together.

In Colorado, the parasitic ant *Sympheidole elecebra* uses *Pheidole ceres* as its host. This parasitic ant has no workers of its own and is considered a degenerate form of parasite. The workers of *Pheidole* collect seeds and are, in one sense, harvester ants. Robert E. Gregg collected

Harvester ants removing a cigarette stub left on their mound.

seeds of wallflower, switchgrass, narrowleaf goosefoot, alfilaria, sand dropseed, and Kentucky bluegrass from the galleries of these ants.

The organization of raids by slave-making species of ants has received considerable study, particularly by European myrmecologists. There is much diversity of method and behavior between the members of different ant families.

Some species use scouts that locate host nests. Other species locate their objective by large numbers of searchers that stir their fellow workers to attack. A Russian slave maker, *Rossomyrmex proformicarium,* is reported to run in pairs, one worker carrying another over its head, as they proceed in file to the host nest. The slavemaker *Harpegoxenus americanus* hardly has any organization in its raids. According to L. G. Wesson, raids are sometimes made by a single ant.

Undoubtedly many people have witnessed slave raids of *Polyergus lucidus* and other ants without knowing what they were seeing. A raid on *Formica nitidiventris,* for example, might appear to be nothing more than a column of ants moving through the grass on their daily round of food collecting.

But close observation may reveal that the column eventually arrives at a nest occupied by other ants of a different size and color. The raiders then enlarge the nest entrance and pour in by the hundreds. Within half a minute the raided ants come running out. Soon they are followed by the raiders, carrying larvae and pupae in a straggling column strung out for many yards on the way to the home nest. Usually the raid is completed in an hour or less.

Some raids are more or less peaceful affairs. Others end in mighty battles that may last for hours. The black *Formica fusca* ants frequently defend their colonies against raids by the red slavers, *Formica subintegra.* The battle results in so many dead and dying ants that the ground is dotted with their dismembered bodies. Heads are severed, legs are clipped, and the armored bodies are dented by crushing mandibles.

War is not always inevitable between different kinds of ants or be-

Harvester ant country in the Oregon desert.

tween ants and other creatures. In fact, most of the relationships
between ants and other insects, between ants and larger animals, and
ants and plants are so artful that they are seldom observed.

The carpenter ants that live in the sticks of cherry wood in my back
yard have dozens of associates with which they seem to live on an
amicable basis. When I lift the pieces of wood a motley assemblage
of pill bugs, millepedes, spiders, centipedes, beetles, and worms scurry
for cover along with the ants.

I have sifted the several bushels of twigs and debris from a large
thatching ant mound and found such an assemblage of insects and
other creatures as only a specialized taxonomist of the lower orders of
life could identify. But I have recognized representatives of such groups
as the diplopods or millepedes, ground beetles, annelids, wood-boring
beetles, snout beetles, fly larvae, and carpenter ants. Carcasses of other
insects distributed throughout the rubble were exceedingly numerous
and probably represented scraps from the ants' table that had been
buried in the trash heap. These scraps are evidence of the ants' contact
with the external environment.

Ants are so universally distributed and abundant that they come in
close contact with practically all living things that exist on land. Through
these contacts they become involved in relationships with plants and
animals that range through many degrees of complexity and dependence.

Ants, like other living creatures, are dependent either directly or indirectly on plants. Many ants use plant parts for construction materials.
Many use sap, nectar, and other exudates directly as food. Indirectly,
they obtain sweet substances through aphids, coccids, and other sucking
insects. They also obtain the flesh of insects, dead birds, and mammals
that in turn have obtained their food either directly or indirectly from
plants.

These different adaptations of different ants impel them to live in
different habitats according to their specific needs. Robert E. Gregg has
pointed out that, in addition to food in the ant's immediate niche,

community, or habitat, the factors of temperature, moisture, light, soil, reactions of the species to its environment, and coactions among ants and other wildlife determine their success or failure.

The impact of ants on the environment never has been adequately measured. The parasol and other leaf-cutting ants are capable of denuding a tree of its leaves or a garden of its vegetables overnight. But they never succeed in reducing the jungle to bare ground.

It has been said that harvester ants clear so much forage from their nest surroundings that they compete with game animals. But they did not keep sixty million bison, forty million pronghorn antelope, and countless millions of prairie dogs from existing originally on the plains and prairies. My own investigations indicate that harvester ants do not initiate forage depletion on range lands. Instead, their populations are closely related to plant successions that occur after the pressure of over-grazing, particularly by domestic livestock, has been released.

In a study of harvester ant clearings in the Raft River Valley of southern Idaho, Lee A. Sharp and William F. Barr found a greater total area of ground denuded on poor-condition than on good-condition saltbush ranges. They concluded that increased ant activity was a result rather than a cause of poor range condition.

Harvester ants on the original prairie undoubtedly served a useful purpose in the web of life by perpetuating the forbs and short-lived grasses that appear in plant-succession stages following fire, drought, dust deposition, and temporary overgrazing by game animals. Frequently the only substratum favorable for these intermediate-stage plants is the

The world of the ant once included bison, which grazed plants the ants used.

A gravel mound with dome-shaped granaries.

periphery of the cleared circles around large ant mounds.

Ants influence plant succession by selecting scarce seeds of plants such as globe mallow, evening primrose, and chaenactis and by not collecting all the seeds of abundant species. In fact, ants could hardly affect the total supply of abundant plants such as woolly plantain, which Lloyd Tevis has estimated to produce 1,254,165,300 seeds per acre in the California and Mexican deserts.

Dr. L. R. Jones once showed me a pasture area near Fort Collins, Colorado, that contained none of the western wheatgrass plants native to the area. After he poisoned the ants, wheatgrass grew abundantly in the same area two years later.

On the other hand, ants are influenced by plant succession through changes in their food supply and by lethal factors such as shading. M. V. Brian reports that stands of bracken that appeared after tree cutting reduced the range of *Formica rufa* in the English Lake District. He also reported that *Lasius flavus* was shaded out by heather and tall oatgrass in lightly grazed grasslands.

The dynamics of plant successions have been investigated for innumerable plant communities the world over. But few people have studied the relations of ants to these successions. For one who wants an absorbing and instructive hobby, and one that may have practical application, an investigation of ants and plant succession can be made in any vacant lot or woodland anywhere in our country.

128

Ants and Men

MEN MAY HAVE INHABITED the earth for a million years, but ants have been here at least one hundred million years. At the time of the Tertiary, ants had already developed societies, had worker castes, cared for aphids, and had insect guests in their nests.

The records of ancient ants are written in fossils. Many prehistoric species are preserved in amber, which is the fossilized resin of trees. This sticky substance oozed out of ancient evergreen trees, just as it does today, and trapped ants, flies, and other insects. Their minute details are so well preserved that we can see their close resemblance to modern ants.

Fossil ants also are preserved in rocks in various parts of the world. Some of the best-known ant fossils have come from the Bagshot beds of Bournemouth, England; from the Oligocene formations of Gurnet

Fossil amber ants caught in resin that seeped from an injured pine tree. Ants seem to derive food from resins.

Bay, Isle of Wight; and from Sicilian amber. F. M. Carpenter, more than thirty-five years ago, wrote an extensive account of North American fossil ants, with particular attention to those from the Florissant area in Colorado and the Green River shales in Wyoming.

I have visited the fossil beds near Florissant, Colorado, where magnificent fossil stumps of giant redwood trees can be seen. I can imagine the luxuriant forests and swamps where the ancient ants once lived. Now, in the Florissant country, honey ants make their symmetrical craters in the open pine woods.

The fossil ants in amber certainly lived in forests and possibly in the trees themselves. Fossil ants in rocks are mostly winged males and females that were blown into lakes, washed in by floods, or brought to earth by volcanic ash and then covered by sediments and preserved. Ants that dwelt in ancient deserts were not likely to be preserved as fossils, and consequently we have no reliable records of their characteristics.

Fossil ants are of special interest to scientists since the paleontological record sheds light on their family relationships and explains many of the changes in physical structure, learning ability, and habits of present-day ants.

Two worker ants, preserved in amber, collected by Mr. and Mrs. Edmund Frey in New Jersey recently have been characterized by Edward O. Wilson, Frank M. Carpenter, and William L. Brown, Jr., as the first ants of Upper Cretaceous age. These fossil ants, *Sphecomyrma freyi,* form a link between some of the earliest known wasps and the most primitive myrmecioid ants. They are of exceptional interest since they definitely extend the existence of social life in insects back to approximately one hundred million years.

It has been speculated that the ancestors of all ants first appeared in the plains of Central Asia more than a hundred million years ago. From there they spread east through Japan and Siberia to North America and west to Europe and Britain. The primitive ants that moved

Australian bull ant: a primitive hunting ant. (Ed Slater)

to New Zealand and Australia became separated from their relatives on other continents some sixty-five or seventy million years ago. Like many other animals in Australia, the ants retained their primitive characters and did not evolve to the complicated societies we find in the northern hemisphere today.

Ants furnish material for fascinating contemplation when one becomes familiar with the different kinds and then views their structure and habits in the light of their developmental history. The ponerines, or primitive ants, for example, are hunters, just as early men were hunters. Their queens have heavy integuments, or armor, which limits expansion of their gasters and therefore their egg-laying capacities. Hence their colonies are relatively small.

The highly developed ants have thin integuments, are capable of producing large colonies, have greater intelligence, since their thin armor permits closer contact of the senses with the environment. Along with intellectual development, ants also have become more specialized in their habits of living.

131

Many ants favor caterpillars, especially dead ones, in their diet.

Man's interrelationships with ants have centered mainly around agricultural disturbances, which have caused ant distributions to change, and around control of ants because they seem to disturb what man wants for himself alone. Little consideration has been given to the usefulness of ants.

Ants have an important place in nature. They are soil builders. Some are agriculturalists in the sense that they plant seeds unwittingly and thereby maintain botanical mixtures of species that best perpetuate a diversified and desirable flora.

Ants are among the most efficient eaters of other insects and therefore are important in maintaining balance among grazing creatures of low order. As biological controls they keep populations of spiders, termites, and other insects in balance. In a larger way, arboreal ants in the tropics protect their trees so efficiently that forests are not defoliated

Horned toads of the plains and deserts also favor many ants. (Joe Van Wormer)

by insects that might change the whole aspect of the forest environment.

Many plants have nectaries that secrete honeydew. These are found on elderberries, oaks, acacias, and many other plants. It is believed by some scientists that ants are attracted to these nectaries and thereby serve a useful purpose by fighting off caterpillars and other destructive insects.

Ants are among the most efficient of scavengers. Not only do they eat numberless bodies of dead insects but they also convert organic material into substances that are useful for other organisms. Ants themselves, their larvae, and their cocoons also serve as food for small mammals, fishes, reptiles, arachnids, and birds and thus enter the food chain that is incessantly followed in the economy of nature.

Studies of ant-aphid relationships in Germany have shown that more aphids are found in forests where ants are present and that bees collect 1.6 times as much honeydew from ant-inhabited forests as from ant-free forests. Since the bees are aided by the ant-tended aphids, it might be argued that the ants indirectly aid the flowering plants that are pollinated by the bees.

In the forests of the Pacific Northwest as much as 70 per cent of the spruce and hemlock reproduction develops on rotten logs. Carpenter ants aid in this rotting process by excavating wood and by introducing fungi and moisture into the logs, which speeds up the decay process. It has been observed that ants in other regions prefer certain species of logs. By speeding selective decay and providing different kinds of surface-soil material, the ants promote germination of some plants instead of others. Thus they influence botanical composition and succession in forests.

Insofar as man is a part of nature, he sometimes makes direct use of ants. Honey ants are used as a source of sweetness by various people in the Southwest and in Mexico. Neal A. Weber reported (1966) that the Indians of Central and South America have long used the large females of *Atta* as food. The gasters filled with eggs undoubtedly have nutritional value. Chocolate-covered ants are sold in the gourmet departments of stores in the United States.

Man generally gives greatest attention to ants when they interfere with his desires or affect his economy. The depredations of ants were noted in 1559 by Bartolomé de Las Casas, who described the failure of the Spaniards to grow cassava and citrus trees in South America because of leaf-cutting ants, probably *Atta cephalotes.* Later, Latin-American countries passed laws naming certain ant species as plague animals.

Man himself is to blame for most of the damage caused by ants. He has introduced destructive foreign species such as the Argentine ant, *Iridomyrmex humilis,* and the fire ant, *Solenopsis saevissima richteri.* In their native countries these ants have not been considered to be particularly destructive. But in new environments they become pests because they have not settled into balance with predators and natural food conditions.

Man also has contributed to the problem by changing the face of the earth through denudation of original vegetation, farming new crops, indiscriminate killing of predators with sprays and chemicals, and drastically disturbing populations of insects. Furthermore, he has taken little time to investigate the basic reasons for certain insect species acquiring pest status.

Ants do cause damage in various ways. They sting and bite when people interfere with their activities. Some victims are highly sensitive to ant poison and may be hospitalized if they are allergic to ant venom. There is one report of a baby that was killed in New Orleans by fire ants. Two deaths from harvester ant stings have been reported from Oklahoma. Bees, however, kill many more people each year than ants do in a decade.

Ants may become pests when they protect aphids and other insects that feed on plants useful to man. They also cause damage when they tunnel in the walls and foundations of houses that have not been properly

Ants and fungi destroy logs on which spruce and hemlock trees sometimes germinate, which causes the growing tree to stand high on its roots.

constructed or protected from moisture.

Large ant mounds sometimes become unsightly in lawns and may cause damage to harvesting machinery in hayfields. Occasional reports are heard of ants attacking livestock, but I am inclined to believe some of these are exaggerated by writers searching for sensational article material.

Harvester ants have been accused of destroying forage that otherwise would be available for grazing animals. I have investigated many of these complaints and, having been professionally engaged in range research for thirty years, can say authoritatively that in most instances the cause has been too many cows. The cows overgraze the grasses, a weedy plant cover develops with its seed supply relished by ants, and the ants increase in numbers.

Attempts to control ants have resulted in some notable disturbances of ecosystems. Most notable of these were the early attempts at fire ant control in the South. Millions of dollars were appropriated and spent without adequate consideration of the effects on wildlife. Beneficial insects, game animals, birds, and fishes were slaughtered on thousands of acres by the unwarranted use of chemicals toxic to wildlife in general.

135

When cattle graze so closely that few plants can produce seeds, the harvester ant population is low. It will increase if grazing diminishes.

Applications of dieldrin and heptachlor at the rate of two pounds per acre killed over forty species of wildlife, including snipes, rails, cardinals, brown thrashers, mockingbirds, meadow larks, woodpeckers, rabbits, mice, salamanders, snakes, frogs, and fish.

Consideration now is being given to the use of parasitic ants from South America as a biological control for the fire ants. These parasites cling to the fire ant queens and lay eggs of their own as the queen lays eggs. The workers care for both sets of eggs, and eventually the fire ant colony is weakened and replaced by the parasitic ants.

Many insecticides now are available for ant control. Carbon disulfide sometimes is effective in outdoor control of ants. Because of its flammability and toxicity to man, it should not be used indoors. Many years ago it was poured into harvester ant mounds in Kansas, after which the mounds were covered with galvanized wash tubs to confine the vapor. Thieves stole the tubs.

Rotenone is safe for indoor use and is relatively nontoxic to mammals. When the ants walk through the dust they carry it to their nest mates and thus the colony may be killed. Pyrethrum also is toxic to insects and may be used safely indoors for ant control. Lindane vaporizers sometimes are used in greenhouses, but they are not safe for home use. Long exposure to lindane vapor can cause aplastic anemia, a disease that can be fatal to humans.

Methyl bromide fumigation has been used successfully against leaf-cutting ants. The vapor is applied through tubes thrust into holes in ant colonies. The vapor is highly toxic to humans.

Kepone bait mixed with peanut oil, Bayer 38920 fire ant bait, and Mirex fire ant bait, both of which latter poisons are mixed with corncob grits impregnated with soybean oil, have been found useful in control of fire ants and harvester ants. The Mirex bait pellets are placed around feeder holes or directly on the ant mounds. This latter bait is said to be effective without obvious damage to game birds.

Robert L. Furniss has listed carbon tetrachloride, fly spray, kerosene, diesel oil, turpentine, and coal-tar creosote as deterrents and possible control agents where carpenter ants create a problem in houses. Fumigation with hydrocyanic acid gas has given variable results; it should be applied only by an experienced operator.

For control of carpenter ants outside or under buildings, a 5 per cent chlordane dust or one cup of 44 per cent chlordane emulsion concentrate in five quarts of water may be applied by spraying.

Although ants do considerable damage under certain conditions and occasionally cause annoyance in homes and gardens, it must be remembered that they have their own useful niches in nature. Because of their almost universal presence, their fantastic habits, and the ease with which they can be reared in cages or artificial nests, they make fascinating pets.

Many kinds of artificial nests are possible. They can be made at home or obtained from biological supply houses. The plastic Ant Farms with transparent sides distributed by the Los Angeles firm, Cossman and Levine, Inc., can be obtained in toy stores and department stores. Robert B. Sabin told me that more than ten million of these Ant Farms have been sold. The company keeps thirty-five people occupied as ant

Ant Farms, with ants and food included, can be purchased in stores. (Cossman and Levine, Inc.)

collectors who turn up twenty-five million ants a year to keep the Ant Farms supplied.

Ant watching has been recommended by educators for students of all ages. A surprisingly large number of artificial ant nests are used in hospitals and rest homes for old people to relieve boredom and anxiety. Scientists, of course, for many years have kept ants in their laboratories for psychological studies and for observations of colony activities.

Artificial ant nests should be constructed so the ants can be observed at all times. The most practical homemade nests consist of two panes of glass, about 12 inches square, held upright in grooved strips of wood. A wide base made of wood will keep the structure from tipping. The top should be hinged to permit partial filling with soil or sand and to introduce the ants. The top should have holes for ventilation and for feeding and watering the ants. The holes can be plugged with cotton.

Horizontal nests, 12 to 16 inches long, 8 to 10 inches wide, and 1 inch deep can be made with two or more rooms. If the glass in one room is darkened with cardboard or red plastic, the ants will move into that room. When it needs cleaning, the cover can be moved to the other room and the ants will move. No soil is required, but a slice of moistened sponge should be included since ants cannot live long without water.

Local ants can be dug in the garden or woods and carried home in a covered jar or coffee can. Many nests can be found under stones. If the digging is done quickly the queen, workers, larvae, and cocoons may be obtained.

Further details for starting and maintaining ant colonies are given in Turtox Service Leaflet No. 35, General Biological Supply House; in R. E. Siverly's book, *Rearing Insects in Schools;* in William Morton Wheeler's book, *Ants;* and in other literature on ants and insects. Some of the more complicated ant nests made by scientists are constructed with plaster of Paris or consist of several glass cages connected by tubing, which allows the ants to go from cage to cage.

Ants can be fed many things, depending on the species. Some require

Ants are used in nature-study classes in schools. (Cossman and Levine, Inc.)

An artificial nest made of lantern slide glass is excellent for viewing very small ants.

protein, which can be supplied by giving them finely chopped pieces of insects or hamburger without salt. I feed my thatching ants very small pieces of cheese, bread, white meat of cooked turkey, boiled eggs, sugar, and honey. My harvester ants like cracked seeds, small insects, and dry breakfast cereals.

Ants soon become accustomed to their artificial homes and almost immediately begin construction of tunnels if proper material is available. When they become familiar with the nest odor, and if they are not shaken or disturbed, they do not even take the trouble to identify one another with their antennae. Foreign odors from food, air currents, and other disturbances will make them identify. If greatly disturbed, *Formica* ants may even squirt formic acid on the sides of their cages.

By careful observation one may observe many activities in the ant nest, including regurgitation, transportation of larvae, "birth" of young ants from cocoons, and grooming with legs and tongues. Grooming, incidentally, is a fascinating activity for observation. It has been described in detail by Edward O. Wilson for the Neotropical ant *Daceton armigerum*. Grooming movements included antenna wiping, oral "leg" cleaning, two-front-leg wiping, three-leg wiping, head wiping, abdominal tip cleaning, brood washing, and queen care.

Among other things, I have tried to determine the "firing order" of ant legs while the ant was walking. Some of them move the hind leg on one side, next the middle leg, and then the front leg. The legs on the other side alternate in forward motion in the same sequence. But any leg can operate independently, or the two front legs can move simultaneously. They also use all legs on one side while all legs on the other side remain stationary. This causes the ant to turn like a caterpillar tractor with one track stopped. (This is on glass; on soil it may be different.)

Artificial nests have enabled scientists to make many studies of ant psychology and ant habits. With nests deep in the ground, ants almost defy detailed study.

After several years of effort, researchers in Louisiana succeeded in establishing colonies of the town ant in the laboratory. The ants and their fungus were in transparent plastic containers connected with tubes for runways. The ants readily foraged leaves placed outside their canisters. The queens were seen laying eggs. The larger workers licked leaves prior to placing them on the fungus gardens. Tiny workers took painstaking care of the fungus.

Many studies have been made to test the learning ability of ants. Ants learn simple mazes more rapidly than cockroaches. But ants generally fail when presented with detour problems whereby they are blocked from direct approach to food they can see or smell. Only monkeys and chimpanzees show any degree of success upon exposure to such situations.

Dr. T. C. Schneirla of the Department of Animal Behavior at the American Museum of Natural History placed *Formica* ants and rats in mazes that were identical except for size. Rats learned to avoid the blind alleys in twelve runs; ants required thirty runs.

The secrets of ant travel and food exchange are being unraveled by radionuclide tracers such as radioactive phosphorus and radioactive iodine. T. G. Marples, using a Geiger-Müller detector, demonstrated that the ant *Crematogaster clara* took up the tracer that had been injected into salt-marsh grass stems. Tracer studies also have been used to ferret out the location and extent of tunnels used by ants that seldom appear above ground. The chain of food distribution also has been traced in ant colonies by means of radioactive iodine.

The new methods of chemical analysis by gas chromatography and mass spectrometry now are being used to resolve the nature of chemical secretions of ants. Most social behavior in ants is triggered by chemicals that are discharged at appropriate times. Some of the chemicals produced by ants are terpenes, skatole, citral, citronellol, propyl isobutyl ketone, and formic acid.

Different odorous compounds are produced by different species of ants. Different chemicals also are produced by different sexes and castes in the same species. The queen, for instance, produces her own odors. Soldiers of the myrmecine ant *Pheidole fallax* produce a fecal odor but do not lay odor trails as do the workers.

In addition to odor trails, ants produce chemicals for defense, for alarm, and for recognition of friends and enemies. Even the removal of corpses to the ant cemetery is activated by decomposition products such as long-chain fatty acids and their esters. Hungry larvae of some species produce chemicals that guide nurse ants to their mouth parts.

Ants have many glands for the production of chemicals. The mandibular glands in the head secrete terpenoid alarm substances. The pharyngeal glands, which open into the pharynx near the mouth, have a digestive function. The salivary glands are located in the thorax.

Venom glands in the gaster supply the sting with venom or with formic acid. The anal glands produce substances used either for defense or for alarm. The venom of the fire ant is an amine, possibly $C_{35}H_{73}N$. Venoms of ants, like venoms of snakes, now are being studied to determine possible beneficial uses in medicine. But deciphering the chemical code will require much study before it can be used as a basis for explaining the entire social behavior of ants.

Social behavior in ant societies many times has been described as being similar to human behavior in human society. In support of this concept many fanciful comparisons and parallels have been drawn.

Ants are believed to have developed from simple hunting savages to groups that now include agriculturalists, millers, soldiers, slave makers, and carpenters. These developments have been cited as being similar to the historical development of human society.

George and Jeanette Wheeler have listed other similarities between ants and men, such as cooperation, helpless young, division of labor, highly developed communication, slavery, and warfare. The Wheelers also have listed many differences: number of species, antiquity, progress by evolution, and castes, which are based on anatomical differences in

Ants are sociable creatures and share honey in a jar with one another.

ants and on opinions in men.

Ant societies are essentially female societies in which only certain members can reproduce. In human society most individuals can reproduce.

Communication among ants is largely chemical and instinctive. Among humans it is symbolic, through words by which abstract ideas are conveyed from one to another. Likewise, learning among ants is mostly instinctive and limited.

Most important of all is culture. Ants have none of the tools of culture such as hammers, saws, motors, and factories. Nor do they have any of the symbols of culture such as pictures, money, books, government, schools, and religion. And last of all, ants long ago reached the summit of their intellectual attainment. Man, we hope, is just getting started.

Ant Subfamilies

Ants belong to the family Formicidae of the order Hymenoptera of the class Insecta. Their Hymenopteran relatives include sawflies, ichneumons, chalcids, wasps, and bees. There are differences of opinion among myrmecologists about the number of subfamilies of ants. Some recognize eight and some recognize nine subfamilies.

The taxonomy and keys to North American ants are given in W. S. Creighton's *The Ants of North America*. M. R. Smith's catalog gives references and distributional data about the species of ants. Other references include M. R. Smith, "A Generic and Subgeneric Synopsis of the Male Ants of the United States" and "A Generic and Subgeneric Synopsis of the United States Ants, Based on the Workers." In addition to these, many lists and keys to the ants of different states and countries have been published.

The generally recognized subfamilies of ants are as follows:

Myrmeciinae. Primitive ants found in Australia, represented by the bull ant. The queen is an egg-laying worker that hunts for food during colony founding. These ants are heavily armored, slow moving, and possess powerful stings. They are solitary foragers and are carnivorous in general.

Pseudomyrmicinae. Tropical stinging ants that nest in thorns or in plants. The petiole, or ant's waist, has two segments. The larvae have pockets on their abdomens in which food is placed. The pupae are naked. These ants feed omnivorously.

Ponerinae. These are widespread and common primitive ants with

144

little caste differentiation. The petiole consists of two segments. They are hunters with powerful stings. Like the Myrmeciinae they do not exchange food. Their eggs do not adhere in clusters and so are difficult to move in time of danger. The pupae usually develop in cocoons.

Cerapachyinae. A small group of primitive, sting-bearing, carnivorous ants that are nomadic like army ants. They have specialized larval feeding. The pupae develop in cocoons. These ants apparently developed from the Ponerinae but also have doryline features.

Dorylinae. These are the driver or army ants. The petiole has two segments, but the second is not always distinctly separated from the gaster. These primitive ants have developed the group-foraging method and are highly carnivorous. They live in the tropics where insect and other animal food is abundant. The pupae of some species develop in cocoons and some do not. The queen lacks wings and periodically develops an enormous gaster at egg-laying time. During army marches she walks along with the workers and soldiers.

Leptanillinae. This is a small group of tiny army ants.

Myrmicinae. This group includes many of our familiar ants such as the harvesters and the fungus growers. They live in large colonies and have striking caste differentiation, which varies among genera from polymorphic to dimorphic to monomorphic. All have stings but not all stings are functional. The pupae are naked. These ants follow odor trails. Some species are aphid tenders, some are slave makers, and some are workerless parasites.

Dolichoderinae. A large group of more advanced ants with rather similar feeding and nesting habits among the different genera. The petiole consists of one segment. Larvae are naked. The worker caste mainly has only one form. These ants follow odor trails but do not spray venom. They are characterized by disagreeable odors. Some are called scavenger ants, since they eat the refuse left by other ants. Others eat honeydew, insects, and plant materials. One genus has repletes that store honey in their crops.

145

Formicinae. These are the most advanced ants in structure and diversity of habits. The petiole consists of one segment. They do not sting but can spray venom. Nests are underground, in mounds, or in trees. The helpless larvae are tended by workers and fed by regurgitation. Pupae usually develop in cocoons. The workers are polymorphic, monomorphic, or occasionally dimorphic. These ants are excitable and readily bite and squirt formic acid. Their armor is thin and allows excellent sensory connection with the environment. This subfamily includes aphid tenders, honey ants, slaves, slave makers, silk weavers, and carpenters. Many ants of this subfamily tolerate our cold northern climate.

Bibliography

Allee, W. C. *Cooperation Among Animals.* New York: Henry Schuman, 1951.

Allen, Durward L. "Poison from the air; fire ant program," *Field and Stream,* 63:49–51 (February, 1959).

Arnett, W. Harold. *Investigations on the Harvester Ant,* Pogonomyrmex occidentalis *(Cresson), on Nevada Rangelands.* Progress Report, University of Nevada, Department of Plant Science, Circular No. 36, 1962.

Auclair, Jacques L. "Aphid feeding and nutrition," *Annual Review of Entomology,* 8:439–40 (1963).

Beamer, R. H., and Charles D. Michener. "Mutual relationships between leaf-hoppers and ants," *Journal of the Kansas Entomological Society,* 23:110–13 (1950).

Brian, M. V. "Caste determination in social insects," *Annual Review of Entomology,* 2:107–20 (1957).

————. "Serial organization of brood in Myrmica," *Insectes Sociaux,* 4:101–210 (1957).

————. *Social Insect Populations.* London and New York: Academic Press, 1965.

————. "The stable winter population structure in species of *Myrmica,*" *Journal of Animal Ecology,* 19:119–23 (1950).

Brown, W. L. "A few ants from the Mackensie River delta," *Entomological News,* 60:99 (1947).

————. "The release of alarm and attack behavior in some New World army ants," *Psyche,* 67:24–27 (1960).

Burns, W. A. "Try an ant palace," *Parents' Magazine,* 33:98 (June, 1958).

147

Burr, Malcolm. *The Insect Legion: The Significance of the Insignificant,* 2nd ed. London: James Nisbet, 1954.

Callison, Charles. "Fire ant program gets clearance," *Audubon Magazine,* 64:264–65 (September, 1962).

Carpenter, F. M. "The fossil ants of North America," *Bulletin of the Museum of Comparative Zoology,* Harvard College, 70:1–66 (1930).

Cavill, G. W. K., and D. L. Ford. *The Chemistry of Ants.* London: Chemistry and Industry, 1953.

——— and Phyllis L. Robertson. "Ant venoms, attractants, and repellents," *Science,* 149:1337–45 (September 17, 1965).

———, ———, and F. B. Whitfield. "Venom and venom apparatus of the bull ant, *Myrmecia gulosa* (Fabr.)," *Science,* 146:79–80 (1964).

Chapman, J. A. "Predation by Vespula wasps on hilltop swarms of winged ants," *Ecology,* 44:766–67, (1963).

———. "Swarming of ants on western United States mountain summits," *Pan-Pacific Entomologist,* 30:93–102 (1954).

Chauvin, R. "Le comportement de construction chez *Formica rufa,*" *Insectes Sociaux,* 5:273–82 (1958).

Cole, Arthur C. "The ant, *Pogonomyrmex occidentalis* (Cresson), associated with plant communities," *Ohio Journal of Science,* 32:10–20 (1932).

———. "The ants of Utah," *American Midland Naturalist,* 28:358–88 (1942).

Creighton, William S. "The ants of North America," *Bulletin of the Museum of Comparative Zoology,* Harvard College, 104:1–585 (1950).

——— and R. H. Crandall. "New data on the habits of *Myrmecocystus melliger* Forel," *Biological Review,* City College of New York, 16:2–6 (1954).

Crowell, H. H. "Control of the western harvester ant, *Pogonomyrmex occidentalis,* with poisoned bait," *Journal of Economic Entomology,* 56:295–98 (1963).

Dreyer, W. A. "The effect of hibernation and seasonal variation of temperature on the respiratory exchange of *Formica ulkei* Emery,"

Physiological Zoology, 5:301–31 (1932).

———. "Further observations on the occurrence and size of ant mounds with reference to their age," *Ecology,* 23:486–90 (1942).

———. "Seasonal weight and total water content of the mound-building ant, *Formica exsectoides* Forel," *Ecology,* 19:38–49 (1938).

Echols, Hamp W. "Assimilation and transfer of Mirex in colonies of Texas leaf-cutting ants," *Journal of Economic Entomology,* 59:1336–38 (1966).

Eisner, T., and Edward O. Wilson. "Radioactive tracer studies of food transmission in ants," *Proceedings of the Tenth International Congress of Entomology,* Montreal, 2:509–13 (1958).

Farb, Peter. "Ordeal by sting," *Today's Health,* 38:31, 69–72 (1960).

Furniss, Robert L. *Carpenter Ant Control.* Extension Circular 627, Oregon State College, Corvallis, April, 1957.

Gannon, Robert. "How to have ants in the house," *Popular Science Monthly,* 175:152–53 (August, 1959).

Geiger, Rudolf. *The Climate near the Ground.* Cambridge, Mass.; Harvard University Press, 1959.

Goetsch, Wilhelm. *The ants.* (Translation of *Die Staaten der Ameisen,* Springer-Verlag, 1953). Ann Arbor, Mich.: University of Michigan Press, 1957.

Gregg, Robert E. *The Ants of Colorado.* Boulder, Col.: University of Colorado Press, 1963.

———. "The ants of northeastern Minnesota," *American Midland Naturalist,* 25:747–55 (1946).

———. "The origin of castes in ants with special reference to *Pheidole morrisi* Forel," *Ecology,* 23:295–308 (1942).

Haskell, P. T. *Insect Sounds.* Chicago: Quadrangle Books, 1961.

Hodson, E. S. "An ecological study of the behavior of the leaf-cutting ant *Atta cephalotes,*" *Ecology,* 36:293–304 (1955).

Holmquist, A. M. "Notes on the life history and habits of the mound building ant, *Formica ulkei* Emery," *Ecology,* 9:70–87 (1928).

———. "Studies in arthropod hibernation. II. Hibernation of the ant, *Formica ulkei* Emery," *Physiological Zoology,* 1:325–58 (1928).

Holt, S. J. "On the foraging activity of the wood ant," *Journal of Animal Ecology,* 24:1–34 (1955).

Hoyt, J. S. Y. "Feeding technique of the pileated woodpecker," *Bulletin of the Massachusetts Audubon Society,* 34:99–103 (1950).

Hutchins, Ross E. "Acacia is an ant palace," *Natural History,* 66:496–99 (November, 1957).

———. *Insects.* Englewood Cliffs, N.J.: Prentice Hall, 1966.

———. "Living honey jars of the ant world," *National Geographic Magazine,* 121:405–11 (1962).

Huxley, Julian, *Ants.* New York: Jonathan Cape and Robert Ballou, 1938.

Ivor, Hance Roy. "The enigma of bird anting," *National Geographic Magazine,* 110:105–19 (July, 1956).

Jackson, W. B. "Microclimatic pattern in army ant bivouac," *Ecology,* 38:276–85 (1957).

Jacobson, Martin. *Insect Sex Attractants.* New York: Interscience (Wiley), 1965.

Jander, Rudolf. "Insect orientation," *Annual Review of Entomology,* 8:95–114 (1963).

Jones, C. R. *Ants and Their Relation to Aphids.* Colorado Agricultural College Experiment Station Bulletin 341, 1929.

Kannowski, Paul B. "The use of radioactive phosphorus in the study of colony distribution of the ant *Lasius minutus,*" *Ecology,* 40:162–65 (1959).

——— and P. M. Kannowski. "The mating activities of the ant *Myrmica americana* Weber," *Ohio Journal of Science,* 57:371–74 (1957).

Karlson, P., and A. Butenandt. "Pheromones (ectohormones) in insects," *Annual Review of Entomology,* 4:39–58 (1959).

King, Calvin. *Harvester Ant Forage Utilization Studies in the Big Horn Basin of Wyoming.* Wyoming Game and Fish Commission, W-27-R-15, 1962.

Krill, J. "Fighting the fire ant," *Popular Mechanics Magazine,* 110:112 (November, 1958).

Lane, Frank W. "The Mystery of Bird Anting," pp. 163–77 in *Animal Wonder World.* New York: Sheridan House, 1951.

Larson, Peggy P. and Mervin W. *All About Ants.* Cleveland: World Publishing Company, 1965.

Bibliography

Law, John H., Edward O. Wilson, and James A. McCloskey. "Biochemical polymorphism in ants," *Science,* 149:544–45 (July 30, 1965).

Mann, William M. *Ant Hill Odyssey.* Boston: Little, Brown and Company, 1948.

———. "The ants of the Fiji Islands," *Bulletin of the Museum of Comparative Zoology,* Harvard College, 64:401–99 (1921).

Markin, G. P. "Lead-solder alloy casting technique for studying the structure of ants' nests," *Annals of the Entomological Society of America,* 57:360–62 (1964).

Marples, T. G. "A radionuclide tracer study of arthropod food chains in a Spartina salt-marsh ecosystem," *Ecology,* 47:270–77 (1966).

McCluskey, E. S. "Daily rhythms in harvester and Argentine ants," *Science,* 128:536–37 (1958).

McCook, Henry Christopher. *The Honey Ants of the Garden of the Gods and the Occident Ants of the American Plains.* Philadelphia: J. B. Lippincott Company, 1882.

———. *The Agricultural Ant of Texas.* Philadelphia: Academy of Natural Sciences, 1879.

McGregor, E. C. "Odour as a basis for oriented movements in ants," *Behaviour,* 1:267–96 (1948).

Michener, Charles D. and M. H. *American Social Insects, a Book about Bees, Ants, Wasps, and Termites.* New York: D. Van Nostrand Company, 1953.

Morley, Derek Wragge. *The Evolution of an Insect Society.* London: George Allen and Unwin, Ltd., 1954.

Moser, John C. "The case of the innocent ants," *Forests and People,* Fourth Quarter, 1960.

———. "Contents and structure of *Atta texana* nest in summer," *Annals of the Entomological Society of America,* 56:286–91 (1963).

———. "Probing the secrets of the town ant," *Forests and People,* Fourth Quarter, 1962.

Odum, Eugene P., and A. J. Pontin. "Population density of the underground ant *Lasius flavus* as determined by tagging with P^{32}," *Ecology,* 42:168–88 (1961).

Peters, H. S. "Late news from the fire ant front," *Audubon Magazine,* 62:54–56 (1960).

Réaumur, René Antoine Ferchault de. *The Natural History of Ants.* Translated by William M. Wheeler. New York: Alfred A. Knopf, 1926.

Riordan, D. F. "The location of nests of carpenter ants *(Camponotus spp.)* by means of a radioactive isotope," *Insectes Sociaux,* 7:353–55 (1960).

Rosenberg, B. "Don't look down on the ant," *Science Digest,* 34:27–30 (1953).

Roy, J. H. "City of tinyville," *Negro History Bulletin,* 19:166–67 (1956).

Rozen, Jerome G., Jr., and Barbara L. "Pit-digging predator," *Natural History,* 71:45–51 (1962).

Rudd, Robert L. *Pesticides and the Living Landscape.* Madison, Wisc.: University of Wisconsin Press, 1964.

Scherba, G. "Moisture regulation in mound nests of the ant *Formica ulkei* Emery," *American Midland Naturalist,* 61:499–509 (1959).

———. "Mound temperatures of the ant *Formica ulkei* Emery," *American Midland Naturalist,* 67:373–85 (1962).

———. "Nest structure and reproduction in the mound building ant *Formica opaciventris* Emery in Wyoming," *Journal of the New York Entomological Society,* 69:71–87 (1961).

Schneirla, T. C., R. Z. Brown, and F. Brown. "The bivouac or temporary nest as an adaptive factor in certain terrestrial species of army ants," *Ecological Monographs,* 24:269–96 (1954).

Schwiebert, Ernest G. "Ants can make trout say uncle," *Field and Stream,* 64:53–55, 106–107 (1961).

Sharp, Lee A., and William F. Barr. "Preliminary investigations of harvester ants on southern Idaho range lands," *Journal of Range Management,* 13:131–34 (1960).

Siverly, R. E. *Rearing Insects in Schools.* Dubuque, Iowa: William C. Brown Company, 1962.

Smith, M. R. "Family Formicidae, pp. 778–875 in *Hymenoptera of America North of Mexico—Synoptic Catalog* ed. by C. F. W. Musebeck, K. V. Krombein, and H. K. Townes, U. S. Department of Argiculture Monograph 2, 1951.

———. "Family Formicidae, pp. 108–62 in *Hymenopters of America North of Mexico—Synoptic Catalog—First Supplement*" ed. by

Bibliography

K. V. Krombein, U. S. Department of Agriculture Monograph 2, 1958.

———. "A generic and subgeneric synopsis of the male ants of the United States," *American Midland Naturalist,* 30:273–321 (1943).

———. "A generic and subgeneric synopsis of the United States ants, based on the workers," *American Midland Naturalist,* 37:521–647 (1947).

Spangler, Hayward G. "Ant stridulations and their synchronization with abdominal movement," *Science,* 155:1687–89 (1967).

Staples, F. A. "Build an ant house," *Recreation,* 46A:44 (April, 1953).

Stumper, R. "Radiobiologische Untersuchungen über den socialen Nahrungshaushalt der Honigameise *Proformica nasuta* (Nyl)," *Naturwissenschaften,* 24:735–36 (1961).

Sudd, J. H. "Communication and recruitment in Pharaoh's ant, *Monomorium pharaonis* (L.)," *Animal Behaviour,* 5:104–109 (1957).

———. "The foraging method of Pharaoh's ant, *Monomorium pharaonis* (L.)," *Animal Behaviour,* 8:67–75 (1960).

Talbot, Mary. "A comparison of flights of four species of ants," *American Midland Naturalist,* 34:504–10 (1954).

———. "Distribution of ant species in the Chicago region with reference to ecological factors and physiological toleration," *Ecology,* 15:416–39 (1934).

———. "Flight activities of the ant *Dolichoderus (Hypoclinea) mariae* Forel," *Psyche,* 63:135–39 (1956).

———. "Mounds of the ant *Formica ulkei* at the Edwin S. George Reserve, Livingston County, Michigan," *Ecology,* 42:202–205, (1961).

———. "Population studies of the ant *Prenolepis imparis* Say," *Ecology,* 24:31–44 (1943).

——— and C. H. Kennedy. "The slave-making ant, *Formica sanguinea subintegra* Emery, its raids, nuptial flights and nest structure," *Annals of the Entomological Society of America,* 33:560–77 (1940)

Teale, Edwin Way. *Days Without Time.* New York: Dodd, Mead & Company, 1948.

Terres, John K. *The Wonders I See.* Philadelphia: J. B. Lippincott Company, 1960.

Tevis, Lloyd P., Jr. "Interrelations between the harvester ant *Veromessor pergandei* (Mayr) and some desert ephemerals," *Ecology,* 39:695–704 (1958).

Van Dresser, C. "Man vs. ant; fire ant menace," *American Forests,* 64: 14–15 (1958).

Waloff, N. "The effect of the number of queens of the ant *Lasius flavus* (Fab.) on their survival and the rate of development of the first brood," *Insectes Sociaux,* 4:391–408 (1957).

Way, M. J. "Mutualism between ants and honeydew-producing Homoptera," *Annual Review of Entomology,* 8:307–44 (1963).

———. "Studies on the association of the ant *Oecophylla longinoda* (Latr.) *(Formicidae)* with the scale insect *Saissetia zanzibarensis* (Williams) *(Coccidae),*" *Bulletin of Entomological Research,* 45:113–34 (1954).

Weber, Neal A. "The biology of the thatching ant, *Formica rufa obscuripes* Forel, in North Dakota," *Ecological Monographs,* 5: 165–206 (1935).

———. "Fungus-growing ants," *Science,* 153:587–604 (1966).

———. "Tourist ants," *Ecology,* 20:442–46 (1939).

Weir, J. S. "Egg masses and early larval growth in *Myrmica,*" *Insectes Sociaux* 6:187–201 (1959).

Wesson, L. G. "Contributions to the natural history of *Herpegoxenus americanus* Emery," *Transactions of the Entomological Society of America,* 65:97–122 (1939).

Wheeler, George C. and Jeanette. *The Ants of North Dakota.* Grand Forks, N. D.: University of North Dakota, 1963.

Wheeler, William Morton. *Ants—Their Structure, Development and Behavior.* New York: Columbia University Press, 1910; rev. ed., 1960.

———. *Demons of the Dust.* New York: W. W. Norton & Company, 1930.

———. "Studies of neotropical ant-plants and their ants," *Bulletin of the Museum of Comparative Zoology,* Harvard College, Vol. XC, No. 1 (1942).

Bibliography

Wight, J. Ross, and James T. Nichols. "Effects of harvester ants on production of a saltbush community," *Journal of Range Management*, 19:68–71 (1966).

Willard, J. R., and H. H. Crowell. "Biological activities of the harvester ant, *Pogonomyrmex owyheei*, in Central Oregon," *Journal of Economic Entomology*, 58:484–89 (1965).

Willis, Edwin O. "Interspecific competition and the foraging behavior of plain-brown woodcreepers," *Ecology*, 47:667–72 (1966).

Wilson, Edward O. "Behavior of *Daceton armigerum* (Latreille), with a classification of self-grooming movements in ants," *Bulletin of the Museum of Comparative Zoology*, Harvard College, 127:401–22 (1962).

———. "Chemical communication among workers of the fire ant *Solenopsis saevissima* (Fr. Smith)," *Animal Behaviour*, 10:134–64 (1962).

———. "Chemical communication in the social insects," *Science*, 149:1064–71 (1965).

———. "A monographic revision of the ant genus *Lasius*," *Bulletin of the Museum of Comparative Zoology* (Harvard College), 113:1–199 (1955).

———. "The origin and evolution of polymorphism in ants," *Quarterly Review of Biology*, 28:136–56 (1953).

———. "The social biology of ants," *Annual Review of Entomology*, 8:345–68 (1963).

——— and T. Eisner. "Quantitative studies of liquid food transmission in ants," *Insectes Sociaux*, 4:157–66, (1957).

———, Frank M. Carpenter, and William L. Brown, Jr. "The first mesozoic ants," *Science*, 157:1038–40 (1967).

Young, J., and D. E. Howell. *Ants of Oklahoma*. Oklahoma Agricultural Experiment Station Miscellaneous Publication MP71, 1–42, 1964.

Zahl, Paul A. "Plants that eat insects," *National Geographic Magazine*, 119:642–59 (1961).

Zajonc, Robert B. "Social facilitation," *Science*, 149:269–74 (1965).

Index

Italic page numbers indicate illustrations.

Index

Index